Effective Medical Writing

By Thomas A. Buckingham, MD, PhD

"Every word is endowed with a spirit, therefore the speaker or expounder should carefully deliver his words at the appropriate time and place, for the impression which each word maketh is clearly evident and perceptible... "

(<u>Tablets of Baha'u'llah</u>, Pp. 172-173)

Bahá'u'lláh (1994) *Tablets of Bahá'u'lláh*. Wilmette, Illinois, USA: Bahá'í Publishing Trust.

ISBN 978-0-9994351-0-6

Acknowledgements

I would like to express my thanks to my wife, Zarin, who encouraged me during this time-consuming project.

Table of Contents

Introduction

This book grew as an offshoot of my monthly email newsletter, How to Write Medical and Scientific Papers. As of this writing, we have over 6200 subscribers from all parts of the globe. I would like to express my thanks to my readers for their continuing interest and encouragement.

A diverse collection of people are involved in medical writing, including medical professionals and professional communicators. Currently, there is an accelerating and rapid expansion of scientific and medical knowledge taking place throughout the world. There is a pressing need for clear communication of the findings of the numerous scientific studies that make up this body of knowledge. Information overload can lead to confusion and prevent practical application of this knowledge. Professional healthcare communicators, including medical writers, can untangle this knowledge and present it in formats suited to the various audiences that are interested. Most medical writing is usually not meant to entertain and is usually not very lucrative, but it may contain a strong intellectual appeal and useful information.

The definition and role of the medical writer has expanded greatly in recent years. The role of the medical writer can include that of a freelance writer, a physician trying to report clinical results, a biomedical scientist writing a journal article, a professional medical writer working for the pharmaceutical industry, or a manager of a team of medical writers. The tools and technology used by the medical writer have also changed in recent years. The efficient use of information technology is an essential part of medical writing. Some recent advances in this field include the expanded use of the Internet and the use of electronic publishing systems. The medical writer is challenged to keep up with advances and changes in software and technology. In addition to reporting on new medical developments, the medical writer must also be creative. For example, he must be able to brainstorm, start new projects, and create original content. These may be new continuing medical education (CME) programs, monographs or newsletters. In addition, the medical writer might be called on to develop strategic publication plans for the marketing of a product or of an entire product line. The medical writer is responsible for the quality, scientific accuracy, and ethical integrity of his work and must complete assignments on time. Communication skills are important as the medical writer must interact with a variety of people, including scientists, publishers and audiovisual, slide, or transcription vendors. Medical writers also need to be creative and come up with new approaches and ideas.

The ever-expanding volume of medical information being produced by medical research requires efficient communication. There are a variety of audiences interested in this information and these various groups require different approaches. Medical writing and biomedical writing require the development of specialized skills.

Since the Second World War, there has been rapid progress in medical knowledge and the approval of numerous drugs and medical devices for use in many countries. The rapid growth of this information has exceeded the ability of scientists to communicate it to all interested parties. Modern technology allows for rapid dissemination of knowledge, but cannot insure its accuracy or appropriate application. The burden of responsibility for this communication falls to the medical writer, and if he or she carries out this task well, the healthcare professional can deliver up-to-date medical care more rapidly and accurately.

The effect of the medical writer on our current culture is also evident. One can appreciate this by examining current medical textbooks, with their wealth of illustrations and accompanying CD-ROMS, in comparison to medical textbooks of one generation ago. There are also online textbooks now available, which are written by many authors and constantly updated. The overall appearance and amount of information contained in these books has clearly changed. A brief examination of the healthcare section of a public bookstore will reveal a wealth of information not available to the public a short time ago. Thus, medical writers are exerting effects, perhaps unintended, on our culture.

There is a strong focus by the public and the medical professional on pharmaceuticals. This is due to many reasons, including their costs and the perception that medicine can cure the patient's ailment. In addition, there is a regulatory requirement for the approval of pharmaceuticals and medical devices. This places the medical writer who deals with these areas in an important role. If advances in drug therapy are not clearly communicated to the general public, medical professionals, and to regulatory bodies, in the end, the patient cannot benefit. The European Union had created another large medical marketplace with a common regulatory process.

Medical writing must adhere to certain formatting and ethical standards. A wide variety of professionals may be involved in medical writing. These include medical writers, biomedical scientists and engineers, biomedical engineers and regulatory specialists. Now, teams of specialists often work together on some complex medical writing projects, particularly in industry. There is an ever-increasing number of people interested in improving their medical writing skills.

There are number of reasons why medical writing is important. Of course, the clear communication of medical information to patients, physicians and medical professionals is of obvious importance. In addition the communication of medical information on a new drug or medical device to the regulatory body is of clear economic importance. However, there is a secondary benefit of medical writing, which sometimes goes unrecognized. Medical professionals, who practice and perfect their medical writing, will find that their knowledge of this subject matter will improve. In addition, the acquisition of medical writing skills and the act of medical writing helps to organize one's thinking. This secondary effect is often unappreciated and undoubtedly is a beneficial effect. The job of the medical writer is not only to report new information, but also to interpret the implications of that information for his audience. It may be said that no technology has a greater impact on humankind than medical and health technology.

This book will emphasize the basic skills required for effective medical writing. Medical writing skills may be thought of as a series of building blocks that allow one to advance to higher-level activities. These building blocks include such things as good word choice, sentence structure, and paragraph structure. These skills are used to write a medical paper in the required format. Clear presentation of numerical data including tables, graphs and statistics is also an important skill. Medical writing can be considered as a type of critical argument. Of course, the most persuasive argument is the presentation of new data on a medical question. One fundamental skill is the ability to write a scientific paper and have it published in a peer-reviewed journal. This actually involves several complex tasks and skills. Skills in formatting and editing your own paper are also important. Different formats are required for creating documents for regulatory approval, and these are covered in the text. Strategies to have a medical paper published in a peer-reviewed journal will be discussed as well. There are special types of documents such as curriculum vitae and resumes, abstracts for scientific meetings, slide presentations, posters, case reports, and review articles. Promotional material and patient education material is also covered. In addition the book contains several appendices with resources for medical writers, including updated resources on the Internet. It is hoped that the material here will help readers of diverse backgrounds become a better medical writers and communicators.

Chapter 1: Requirements for Good Scientific Writing

Good scientific writing is a skill that can be developed and fostered. I believe that one must become good at reading scientific literature in order to be able to develop these skills. It is necessary to adopt an organized approach to produce good writing. Apart from the necessary writing and language skills, good scientific writing must be ethical.

There are several requirements for good writing:

1. You must know your subject well. If you write about something that you do not know well, your readers will sense this and put your writing aside. You must provide your readers with some reliable and useful information. It is useful to imagine that you are talking to a friend or associate as you write. You can also imagine or "hear" the questions that they might ask and try to answer them in your writing.

2. You must know who your readers are. Will your readers be physicians or scientists working in the same field as you? Will they be laypersons with only a general interest in your subject? How much do they already know about the subject? What do they want to know? Can they use the information that you are giving them and how?

3. You must know how to use the tools of writing. This means you must know the best words, how to write good sentences, and how to organize your thoughts into effective paragraphs. This includes a good knowledge of English grammar, punctuation, spelling, capitalization,

etc. Unfortunately, you cannot rely on friends to review your writing, unless they themselves are experts. Journal editors and copy editors also cannot be relied on to help you with your writing because they are often very busy and not always motivated to help you.

4. You must give the time required for good writing. Papers require editing, polishing and improvement before submission to a scientific journal.

5. Good writing requires that you be sincere. If you try to hide something from your readers or pretend to know something that you do not, this will be apparent.

Of course, good writing is a skill and it will improve with practice. The more writing that you do the better you will be. To improve your ability for future writing projects, you should try to learn more about what makes up good scientific evidence and how it is gathered and to learn more about the elements of a critical argument and how to write one. It is also important to get honest critical judgments from colleagues and to learn how to revise your own writing. There are other ways to improve your writing. One way is to read good medical or scientific writing. Another is to use a good dictionary or thesaurus as you write or read.

Critical Reading of Medical Literature

Of course, medical writers must also be good readers. Their work requires that they read medical papers, books, and other forms of medical literature extensively. This is necessary to obtain source material and the writer must be able to rapidly and accurately determine which material is most valuable. In addition, a detailed examination of the process of critical reading can help the medical writer to improve his own skills and to make sure that his writing will survive a critical reading by his intended audience.

When the reader first scans a medical paper, his first question is usually if the material is relevant to him or her. Most professionals, particularly those in clinical medicine, are busy and do not have time to read irrelevant material. In addition, the volume of new scientific information is large and is growing, and it is impossible for one individual to read all of it. Therefore, we all must use some selection processes to weed out unimportant material and to search out and select material most relevant to our professional needs. Today, this task is rendered more complex by the fact that material now reaches us through many differing channels and media. For example, we now can "read" medical material on the Internet, in medical journals, in textbooks, and on CD-ROMs, or we can also listen to such material on audio programs distributed through various channels.

The ability to critically read the medical literature is considered very important in the medical education of physicians. As medicine is changing rapidly, no university curriculum can anticipate future developments in medicine. It is therefore very important to train physicians and other medical professionals how to read the medical literature in a systematic fashion to keep up with developments in their fields. It may be necessary for medical professionals to create a program to make sure that they receive relevant updated information in their field, either by subscriptions to certain periodicals or by regular searches of the literature via the Internet. A passive approach is not enough. This is further complicated by the fact that ongoing medical education can now be obtained through a variety of media, i.e. Internet, podcasts, and various audiovisual formats.

Relevance

The relevance of any medical literature is usually determined by the title, objectives and summary. This requires that the abstract be quickly scanned. If the material is found relevant to the authors needs, the next step is usually to determine if the material is valid and to make some assessment of its quality. If the material is judged to be relevant and valid, the entire paper may then be read. The reader has the further task of making sure that he completely understands the methods and the results. He then must endeavor to incorporate it into his knowledge base and perhaps to change the way he practices his profession. It should be noted here that it may be difficult to retain all of the information read and even more difficult to put it into use in daily clinical practice.

Obviously, the title is very important in this process. The title must be accurate, concise and attract the interest of the targeted audience; otherwise, the paper will be quickly passed over.

Validity

To determine whether a paper is valid, the reader asks a series of questions. The first goal is to determine whether the results are valid. The reader should search for an explicit statement about the method of randomization. Was this method of randomization open to bias? In general, computer-generated independent randomization is the best approach.

Were all patients that entered the trial accounted for at the end of the trial? All trials have some dropouts, and these cannot be ignored. The results should be reported on an intention-to-treat basis.

Were patients, clinicians, and the study personnel blinded to the treatment assignment? Were all groups similar at the start of the trial? This should be assessed for making statistical comparisons between groups. Apart from the intervention, all groups should be treated equally. To determine this, look for different adjunctive treatments in the different groups.

Did the study have adequate power? A pre-trial power calculation should be made and this should be reported in the study.

The Nature of the Results

How large was the treatment effect? Another way of asking this is to ask, "What is the number needed to treat to save one patient's life?" Will these results help my patients? Are the patients in the trial similar to my patients? To determine this one must consider the inclusion and exclusion criteria used in the study. We must also consider the population from which the sample was taken. Did the authors report adverse events as well as benefits? Are the benefits worth the harm and costs? This is not only an economic question, but also a question of the side effects of the treatment or intervention used. Finally, what would my patients think? This may be difficult to predict and it may be necessary to discuss the study with your patient to find out the answer.

Critical Reading of a Systematic Review

A systematic review is an attempt to identify all evidence on a particular topic and to evaluate the validity of this evidence using quality filters. Sometimes the results can be combined into a single unified result or a meta-analysis. A good source of systematic reviews is the Cochrane database (discussed later).

These reviews function best when the authors address a specific question. If they attempt to address a question, which is too broad, the results will be diluted. The methods section should include a description of how relevant trials were identified and included. A Pubmed or Medline search alone is not sufficient. The results are usually expressed as an odds ratio, a relative risk, or a difference between the means. Is the evidence applicable to my patient population? To answer this question detailed data on adverse effects must be provided. Again, the final and key question is, what effect will these results have on my patients?

Evidence-Based Medicine (EBM)

Judgment is an essential part of EBM. There are some who would like to dichotomize all studies into good and bad. If the "bad" studies were ignored many medical studies would be excluded from our consideration. The truth is that medical studies lie on a continuum between very good and very bad. Another problem with EBM is that there are many times when it is not possible to find evidence relating to a clinical question. Sometimes, the evidence found is towards the poor end of the spectrum. It is also important to keep in mind that published papers and evidence are not always superior to clinical experience.

Organize and Plan Your Scientific Writing

Some authors have a difficult time knowing where to start on a scientific writing project. Initially the task may seem overwhelming because it is complex and confusing. The key to success is to break down the work into a series of smaller tasks, organize the work and then start. You can start by asking 4 questions:

1. What is the message that I am trying to convey?
2. What is the best format to report this message?
3. Who is the best audience to hear this message?
4. What is the right outlet for the presentation of my message? For example, which scientific journal?

Your message should be defined in terms of what scientific question was asked and answered by your work. Normally this idea includes the purpose of your study. Once this is determined, it is easier to answer the following 3 questions.

When writing a medical paper one should consider what the reader needs. The reader is looking for answers to questions and solutions to problems. The clinician needs to know the best antibiotic for the treatment of an unusual infection. Readers not only need the answer to their question, they need to be convinced that this answer is correct. Readers will not use information from a medical paper unless they are convinced that it is correct. In order to do this, the paper must it be based upon the principles of a critical argument. This is a coherent series of reasons, statements, or facts intended to support or establish a certain point of view. In a medical paper, the critical argument consists of a statement of the problem, presentation of the evidence, evaluation of the validity of the evidence, implications of the evidence, and assessment of this validity in the face of conflicting evidence, and finally, conclusion. A scientific paper includes all of these elements and they are arranged in this order.

According to Hill, a well-known biostatistician, the reader of a scientific paper is searching for the answers to four questions: "Why did you start? What did you do? What answer did you get? What does it mean anyway?" The first question is answered in the introduction of the paper. In the introduction you tell the reader why the research was started. What question has not been settled by previous papers? How did this question arise? Then the introduction must make clear what question the research was designed to answer. The introduction should also make clear what population was studied.

The materials and methods section answers the question: how did you carry out the research? This includes the study design, the state or condition that was studied, the subjects, the methods for selecting subjects, interventions, all observations, and statistical procedures used.

The evidence gathered is then presented in the results section. This data should be presented to give as clear an answer as possible to the question posed. The discussion includes previous papers that contain information bearing on the question. This includes papers that have results similar to yours but also should include any papers that have conflicting results. A discussion of the validity of these papers and an assessment of the overall evidence should be made. Finally, a verdict or conclusion is given.

Best Format

Normally scientific writing is presented in a certain specific form. Examples are research articles, case reports, case series, or reviews. Each has a certain format. The specifics of this format vary somewhat from journal to journal but are usually specified in the instructions to authors for that journal. If your message is an original work or observation, you should publish this in a "primary" journal. A primary journal is one in which original research is presented and which is readily available to the scientific community. The specifics of each format (research paper, case series, etc.) will not be covered here, but will be covered in other sections of this book. In general, when original research or observations are presented in a primary journal, enough detail must be given to allow another worker in the field to reproduce the study. Most of these details will be contained in the methods section of the paper and in its references.

Best Audience

Then you must ask yourself: What is the relevance of the message? Is this message more relevant to certain groups? Is this message primarily for specialists or generalists? Will this message change the way science or medicine is practiced? Is this message truly original or does it confirm work previously done? (Note: work confirming the results of others still merits publication).

The Right Scientific or Medical Journal

A consideration of the proper audience will help you find the right journal. Normally physicians and scientists are familiar with the journals in their respective fields. You may wish to broaden your search to include journals that you are not familiar with. Many times, editors of journals in areas related to your subject area are interested in taking articles that are slightly out of their normal topic range.

In addition, you may wish to consider the impact factor of a given journal. "Journal Citation Reports" ranks journals by their relative "impact factors." This is calculated as the number of citations in a given year to papers published in that journal in the preceding 2 years, divided by the number of citable papers the journal published in that same 2 year period. Although not perfect, this gives us some quantitative idea as to the relative intellectual influence of that journal.

Of course, journals with a high impact factor are the most prestigious journals and are the most difficult to get a paper published in. These journals may receive thousands of article submissions per year and generally have a high rejection rate. If you submit an article to such a journal, it may take 6-8 weeks before they respond to you and this response may be a rejection. Thus, you lose time if you submit your paper to the wrong journal. In evaluating your work and presentation, you must try to be objective and not let your ego come into the picture.

Start Early

An organized approach to your writing may start long before you actually start writing. It can start when you are planning your research. One of your first steps will be to conduct a literature search in the area of your interest. Today, with the ready availability of free Medline on the Internet provided by PubMed, this task is relatively easy.

See: https://www.ncbi.nlm.nih.gov/pubmed

You should not trust your memory during this stage, but keep notes and records of the papers that you find. Try to organize the various papers in some logical fashion. You may wish to use one of the excellent software packages available to do this (see software reviews) or you may do this using pen, paper and file folders. One way to do this is to photocopy the articles (or at least the abstracts) and sort them into files.

Data Collection

As your study progresses, you will be collecting data. This is an excellent time to begin organizing your data into tables, figures and graphs. If you do it at this stage, you will save time later. For example, if you need to go back later and create a figure or make a photograph, the original data may be difficult to find and cost you valuable time.

Starting to Write

After you choose your target journal, read the instructions to authors carefully so that you will know what the editors expect. At this stage, you may wish to make an outline before you write the text of the paper. This outline will contain the classical elements of the scientific paper, such as title, abstract, introduction, methods, discussion, references, tables and figures. Modifications to your outline may have to be made according to the instructions to the authors. The outline of a review paper or of a case report may follow quite a different structure. Outlines normally follow some logical sequence such as chronological order, geographic or spatial order, order of importance, general to particular, simple to complex, pro and con (presenting 2 sides of an argument), or cause and effect.

Another approach to writing is to pose questions and then develop logical answers. The answers will then give rise to other questions and so on. This is part of both the scientific process and of the scientific writing process.

You can use brainstorming techniques to produce a list of questions and their possible answers. One approach is to start with a blank sheet of paper and write down the central idea of your paper in the middle of the sheet. Then draw a circle around it. Write down other related ideas in different parts of the paper, each with a circle around it. Then connect these ideas with the central idea and with each other. If you wish, you can use arrows or other symbols to express the relationships between these ideas. This approach can also be effectively used by a small group to generate new ideas. When you are brainstorming, it is important not to stop to criticize the ideas, as this may inhibit the process and the free expression of thoughts.

This is one way to overcome writer's block. When you feel yourself running out of things to say and writing becomes progressively more difficult, then you can adopt several strategies to continue. You can write around the missing information. Missing information may be something as simple as a missing word.   If you keep writing around the problem, many times inspiration will come and the missing information will be supplied. Also, it is a way to avoid losing momentum. Be careful what you eat when you are writing and be careful not to overeat. Sometimes sleep or exercise will help you think about a problem better and bring a solution to mind.

A Systematic Approach to Writing a Paper

Overview

The most efficient way to write a scientific or medical paper is to adopt a systematic approach. An overview of this approach is as follows. First, write the first draft. This should be done quickly without pausing to review the paper. This process is aided if you have organized your scientific data into tables and figures as you were collecting it. Second, produce a second draft. Changes in the second draft focus on the organization and readability of the paper. This may require deletion of redundant or unnecessary material. Finally, in the third draft correct the grammar, style, and spelling errors and make sure that the paper is in compliance with the instructions to authors for your target journal.

The First Draft

Here the author can start with the scientific question that was asked and answered by his paper. This is the central message of the paper. Next, the author chooses the format that he wishes to use. This may be a case report, a review, or a primary article. The author then determines the audience most appropriate for his message and selects the journal based upon this. If your data is organized before you begin writing, it will speed up the process. Try to write the first draft continuously without going back to review it. It also is very helpful to make an outline first. When you write the first draft, you will have your data and statistical analysis in hand. You will also need to do a literature review as well. It is very helpful to have a system for organizing the papers that you are going to cite in your paper. This can be done on index cards or with a software program.

The Second Draft

After the first draft is finished, it is useful to put it aside for a short time (more than 1 day) and then begin to revise it. This step may require deletion of unnecessary material. This requires detachment on the part of the writer. One reason not to begin revising the style of material too early is the fact that some of it should be simply deleted during the second revision stage. It does not make sense to revise material that will be deleted and if you spend a lot of time revising it, you will find it psychologically difficult to delete material that should be removed. You should resist the temptation to correct minor errors of spelling, style, etc. during the early stages.

During this stage, you may have to move material around in your paper. Modern word processors make this easy, however, it is still useful to work from printed drafts. With a printed draft, you can spread out the pages on a desk and can see the entire paper. Some authors actually like to cut out the sections that they wish to move and to move them physically with pieces of paper. It is during this stage that you should ask questions about the content and structure of your paper. For example, does the abstract summarize the paper adequately in the allowed space? Does the introduction set the stage? Do not do all of your revising on the computer. Use paper and red pen to make some of the changes and then put them into the word processor. Use the header function of your word processor to put the date on every page you produce during the drafting process. This makes it easier to track your revisions.

Revision is the Rule

It is important to realize that revision is the rule and not the exception. No one can write a final draft of a scientific paper in one sitting. There is no reason to get discouraged over the need to delete and revise large segments of your work. This is normal and is part of the creative process of writing. It will lead in the end to better writing. The process of writing with the required drafts and revisions can be enjoyed as a creative process, which is a reflection of the author's personality, intellect and training. Your best writing will have an impact on the thinking of your peers.

As your second draft evolves, you will want to contact your coauthors for input. You should insist on written input and keep track of where suggestions and revisions come from by labeling them with the contributor's name and date. Revisions can be sent by email and then copied directly into the text. This makes the process very fast, if you can get your coauthors to respond to you promptly.

Use of Word Processing Software

Word processing software has revolutionized the process of

writing scientific papers. However, there is an art to using word processing software to produce effective scientific writing. Used incorrectly, a computer and its software may slow you down or lead to certain errors. Certain features of this software should only be used late in the revision process. For example, word processing software can make your paper look very good in its early stages, which makes it psychologically difficult to delete parts of the paper that should be deleted. Therefore you must resist the temptation to produce a perfect copy too early in the process.

Most word processing software includes grammar or style checking software. You must not rely on this software too much. I would still use them, but do not let them make you think that your paper is in better condition that it really is. My word processor sometimes freezes suddenly and if I have not saved my work, I may lose it. It is a good idea to get into the habit of saving your work frequently and to make backups. If you are working on several projects, it is also a good idea to develop a systematic way of naming and keeping track of your files. Do not do all revising on the computer. There is a definite advantage to making a printout and to making changes with a pen or pencil. This helps you to see things better and to think about them in a different way. You cannot see the entire paper through a computer screen. The software will let you put a date and number on each page and you should do this during the drafting process. It will help you keep track of your drafts, which should be saved. Sometimes material on an earlier draft sounds better than material on a later draft and needs to be brought back into the paper. I do not recommend putting dates on the pages of the paper that you submit to a journal. You do not want the editor to know that this paper was written 6 months ago and has probably been rejected by at least one journal.

It is very useful to learn the "find and replace" function in your software. This has several applications and allows you to standardize abbreviations and formats throughout a paper efficiently. The spell checker should be used as a last step. You can "teach" your spell checker the vocabulary that you use in your scientific field. Just be sure that you do not misspell new words that you enter into the dictionary. You must be familiar with "cut and paste operations" in your software.

Ethics in Medical Writing

The "Recommendations for the Conduct, Reporting, Editing, and Publication of Scholarly Work in Medical Journals" is the latest version of a document previously known as, "Uniform Requirements for Manuscripts Submitted to Biomedical Journals: Writing and Editing for Biomedical Publication", is a document developed by the International Committee of Medical Journal Editors (ICMJE), and updated on their webpage:

http://www.icmje.org/about-icmje/faqs/icmje-recommendations/

It includes issues related to ethics, editorial issues, and manuscript preparation and submission. These guidelines have been adopted by many biomedical journals and form a convenient and useful standard. The guidelines contain a substantial section on ethics, which I strongly encourage the reader to review. This material on ethics is presented below in abbreviated form.

Authorship

Authorship of biomedical papers carries with it substantial responsibility and obligations. It also is associated with important academic social and financial implications. Normally, authors of biomedical papers should have made substantial contributions to the conception, design, acquisition of the data, or analysis and interpretation of the data. They should also have helped in the drafting of the article or in revising it. Authors should also have the ability to give final approval of the version for publication. In the case of large multicenter groups working together, these issues are slightly more complicated. Such groups should identify individuals to accept responsibility for the manuscript. Some journals also request that one or more authors take responsibility for the integrity of the manuscript as a whole.

All persons listed as authors should qualify for authorship and all those who qualify should be included. The contributors who do not meet the criteria for authorship should be listed in the acknowledgments section. Sometimes individuals who contribute to a paper, but did not meet the criteria for authorship can be listed under headings such as "clinical investigators" and their function or contribution described.

Editors

The editor of a journal is responsible for the entire content of the publication. The editor should establish and maintain editorial policy, and an independent advisory board may be useful in helping him to do this. Editors must defend their editorial freedom. The World Association of Medical Editors has a definition of editorial freedom, which states that editors should have full authority over the editorial content of their journal and that owners should not interfere in the selection or editing of individual articles.

Peer Review

Peer review is a critical assessment of manuscripts by outside reviewers. The value of peer review has not received much study and is still debated by the scientific community. Peer reviewed journals submit most of their papers for outside review.

Conflicts of Interest

The issue of conflicts of interest must be handled properly in order to insure the quality of medical publications and journals. An author, reviewer, or editor may have a conflict of interest when he or she has a financial or personal relationship that could influence his or her actions. These relationships vary from minor to major in their ability to affect judgment. Financial relationships are easy to identify and most likely to affect the credibility of the journal. All participants in this process must disclose any potential conflict of interest. This is true for authors, reviewers, and editors and it applies both to journal articles and to editorials.

When authors submit a manuscript for publication, they must disclose all financial or personal relationships that might influence their work. Many studies receive funding from commercial firms, foundations, or government. This funding and the conditions under which is it is granted, may have a potential to influence publication. Authors and scientists have an obligation to submit good research results for publication, and they also have an obligation to disclose any potential conflict of interest related to that work.

When editors send articles for peer review, they should avoid selecting reviewers who have an obvious potential for conflict of interest. Reviewers also should disclose to the editors any potential conflict of interest before they review the manuscript. If they have a conflict of interest they should disqualify themselves. Editors who make final decision about manuscripts must have no personal bias. In addition, the editorial staff cannot use any information gained from working with manuscripts for private gain or advantage.

Privacy and Confidentiality

Patients have a right to privacy, and therefore identifying information should not be published in medical articles. An exception may be been made if the patient gives written consent. The masking of the eye region in photographs of patients is not an adequate protection of anonymity.

In addition, the authors of medical papers have a right to privacy. The editors must not disclose the contents of their papers or the editorial decisions made regarding these papers. The same obligation applies to reviewers.

Protection of Humans and Animals in Research

When submitting papers on human subjects, the authors must

indicate that the procedures followed were in accordance with the ethical standards of the ethical committee and with the Helsinki Declaration of 1975, revised in 2000. Likewise the, reports on animal experiments, should indicate that institutional and national guidelines for the care and use of animals were followed.

Obligation to Publish Negative Studies

There is a bias not to submit or to publish negative studies. If only positive studies are published, this leads to a bias in interpretation of medical results. Therefore, editors and authors should make every effort to publish negative studies, if they are carefully done and of good quality.

Corrections and Retractions

Sometimes errors are noted in published articles that require publication of a correction. These corrections should include the original citation and be published on numbered pages and listed in the table of contents. A more serious type of problem is the case of scientific fraud. Normally, it is not the editor's responsibility to investigate such cases. However, when they come up, it may be necessary to publish a retraction or expression of concern regarding the affected article.

Copyright

Many journals require authors to transfer copyright to the journal. There are an increasing number of journals, however, that do not require copyright transfer. These are referred to as "open access" journals.

Sponsorship, Authorship, and Accountability

An editorial in the Annals of Internal Medicine highlighted an important potential ethical dilemma in regard to the publication of clinical trials. Publication of clinical research findings in peer-reviewed journals are the basis for treatment decisions in clinical medicine. Readers of these journals assume that this data is presented in an objective and unbiased manner. Clinical trials are powerful tools and must be used with care. Patients participate in clinical trials usually without payment for altruistic reasons. The use of clinical trials purely for marketing purposes is a misuse of this powerful instrument and of the patients' trust.

Many clinical trials are performed to facilitate regulatory approval of a new medical device or drug. These trials are costly, and make up a significant portion of the large budget required to bring a drug to the market. This industry has recognized the need to control costs, and has found that private nonacademic research groups, or contract research organizations (CROs) can do this job efficiently with reduced costs. Clinical investigators who participate in such trials find that they have little or no input into trial design, no access to the raw data, and only a limited role in data interpretation. More concerning is the fact that the results of the completed trial may not be published at all if they are unfavorable to the sponsor's financial interests. The authors of this editorial, who are editors of well-known medical journals, oppose contractual agreements that prevent investigators from examining or publishing data from clinical trials without the consent of the sponsor. Their feeling is that such an arrangement negatively affects the quality of data published in medical journals, and furthermore makes them a party to a potential misrepresentation of the truth. Authorship of a scientific paper requires both accountability and independence.

Authors of biomedical papers may now be required to sign a statement that they have no conflict of interest, and that they were free to examine the data and publish the results without interference from the sponsor.

Obligation to Register Clinical Trials

ICMJE member journals require registration of clinical trials, which start enrollment after July 1, 2005 as a condition for publication. This means the trials should be registered early in the process, before they start. Clinicaltrials.gov is a registry sponsored by the U.S. National Institutes of Health, which currently registers over 250,000 trials in over 200 countries.

Copyright

Most journals ask that the author transfer copyright to the journal. However, there are a number of open access journals that allow authors to keep their copyright. The journal should make its policies clear to the authors.

Duplicate Submissions

Almost all biomedical journals refuse to consider manuscripts that have been submitted to another journal at the same time. The reasons for this are easy to understand: 1) if both journals accept the paper, the question will arise as to who will have the right to publish it, and 2) both journals will expend a lot of work and time in the evaluation of the manuscript using the time of the editor and of peer reviewers.

Occasionally, the editors of journals may deliberately decide to publish the same paper in more than one journal if the paper is very important to the public health. Examples include clinical guidelines from an important professional society or public policy decisions, etc.

Primary journals seek to publish papers which are original and which have not been published before. Readers of these journals also trust that they are not reading work already published elsewhere. The basis of this includes copyright laws, cost-effective use of resources and time, and ethical conduct. Therefore most primary journals have policies stating that they do not wish to receive papers published in whole or in part in other journals. When an author submits a paper, he is usually required to state that his work has not been previously published.

Sometimes discovery of a major therapeutic advance requires publication or notification of a government agency, sponsoring manufacturer, or the public media, but many journals have policies against this unless the editor agrees to it in advance.

Competing Manuscripts based on the Same Study

Occasionally editors may receive manuscripts from the same study. Such papers may be from coworkers who disagree about the analysis and interpretation of the study or from coworkers who disagree on the facts of the study. If the authors disagree on the analysis and interpretation of the study, they should submit a single paper that expresses both opinions. Then process of peer review may resolve this difference, but if not, a single paper with both views may be published or two papers with contrasting views published. If the disagreement is on the methods or actual results, the editors should refuse publication until this issue is resolved. Sometimes papers are received that analyze data available publicly. In this case, each manuscript can be analyzed separately and it may be reasonable to give priority to the manuscript received first.

Correspondence

Many journals offer their readers the possibility to submit comments, questions, or criticisms about articles published by the journal in a correspondence section or column. The authors of such correspondence should declare any conflict of interest and the authors of the published papers should have an opportunity to respond to the correspondence. The editors may edit this correspondence for length, format or errors, but have a responsibility to allow a range of opinion to be expressed. Editors may set time limits for responding to a given article and set policies regarding informing authors, etc.

Supplements and Theme Issues

Many journals often issue supplemental issues, which are issues that deal with a theme or contain papers on a related topic. Supplements can be useful for education or exchange of research information and provide easy access to focused content. However, funding of these issues by industry has to potential to bias the content. Journal editors must exercise care to maintain editorial control over these issues.

Electronic publication

Most biomedical journals now publish in electronic format as well as in a print version. This includes publishing on the Internet. Similar guidelines used for print media should apply also to this form of publication. Advertising must be distinguishable as such. When a journal provides a link to another Web site, this may be seen as an implicit recommendation, and care must be exercised in what links are provided. Electronic publishing is a field that is clearly undergoing changes and will require development of additional policies as time goes by.

Advertising

The ICMJE guidelines state that advertising should not be allowed to influence editorial decisions and that advertising regarding a particular product should not be run next to articles about that product. Biomedical journals should not run ads for products known to be bad for health such as tobacco.

News Media

The popular news media has a strong interest in new medical research. However, the biomedical journals also have an interest in complete and novel publication of their papers. An embargo system has been used to create a level playing field. Under this system, the popular media agrees to hold publication of news until the publication of the scientific paper in question.

References

Davidoff F, DeAngelis CD, Drazen JM, Hoey J, Hojgaard L, Horton R, Kotzin S, Nylenna M, Overbeke AJ, Sox HC, Sox HC, Van Der Weyden MB, Wilkes MS. Sponsorship, authorship, and accountability. Annals of Internal Medicine. 135: 463-66, 2001.

Warner, James. Clinicians' guide to reading psychiatric literature: Therapeutic trials and systematic reviews. Advances in Psychiatric Treatment 8:73-80, 2002.

Chapter 2. Writing Techniques

There are numerous writing techniques that are useful. These can be thought of as building blocks that allow the acquisition of higher skills later and lead to the ability to write complicated scientific papers well. Basic skills include word choice and specialized vocabulary, good grammar, sentence and paragraph structure, and effective use of punctuation. In addition, the medical writer must learn how to format papers, how to use abbreviations, how to format bibliographies, how to report numerical data, how to construct tables and figures, and how to use and report statistics. There are a variety of types of scientific papers, each with specific formatting and writing requirements. These include review papers, editorials, case reports, and many others.

Steps to improve your writing

1. Read good scientific writing.
2. Use your own judgment when you write.
3. Use a good dictionary. A good thesaurus can help also.

To improve your writing ability, you need to learn more about what makes up scientific evidence and how it is gathered, learn more about the elements of a critical argument and how to write one, get honest critical judgments from colleagues and learn how to revise your own writing.

Using Better Words in Your Writing

Better writing starts with attention to using better words, then using better sentences and paragraphs. Asking a colleague how to use a word or to suggest a word instead of looking it up in the dictionary has some disadvantages. You may miss the chance to learn something new. There are several good general dictionaries in English. I particularly like the current version of **Webster's New Collegiate Dictionary**. This dictionary is recommended in the AMA Style Manual. A thesaurus is a book that will suggest words with similar meanings to the one you are considering. Some word processing software have this feature built in. One excellent thesaurus is **Bartlett's Roget's Thesaurus**.

In general, short and simple words are better than long and seldom used words. They are clearer and save the reader time and energy to read. Journal editors and publishers prefer short words because they save space and costs of printing. Concrete terms are also better than abstract words because they refer to things that can be measured and are easier to remember. Of course, in science, anything that can be measured is better. Specific terms are better than general terms most of the time. It is best to avoid the use of jargon or obscure medical terms. Words that are redundant should also be avoided. For example, "blue in color" means "blue."

Improving your Writing: Sentence Structure

This material may be too basic for some of our readers, but I believe that it will be helpful to many. This section builds on the previous sections and talks about how to improve sentence structure in medical writing or in any type of writing. Sentences can be written so that they are very easy to read and carry more impact. However, to do this, one must follow certain strategies or rules.

1. Subject and verb

    Sentences are most effective when they have a strong subject and verb. For greatest impact, the subject should be close to the beginning of the sentence and should be followed closely by the verb.

    Example: "Rapid ventricular tachycardia causes hemodynamic collapse." is stronger than "Rapid ventricular tachycardia, which has various manifestations on the ECG, causes hemodynamic collapse."

2. Use strong verbs whenever possible.

    Strong verbs are verbs of action. Weak verbs are the verbs of being (is, was, were, had been, etc.)

    Example: "Abnormal ECG findings teach us how to interpret ECGs." is better than "Abnormal ECG findings are good teaching tools."

3. Be careful about placement of subordinate clauses.

    It is best to place such clauses at the beginning or end of a sentence and not in the middle.

    Example: "Premature ventricular complexes, because of the increased use of telemetry monitors, are seen more frequently today." is a relatively weak sentence. Instead: "Premature ventricular complexes are seen more frequently today because of ..."

4. Use active voice in preference to passive voice when possible. Sentences in active voice are usually easier to understand than those in passive voice. Also, such sentences are more concise. However, the passive voice is useful when you do not want to call attention to the doer. The doer may be obvious or unimportant.

   Example: "The assembly decided to postpone the vote." is better and shorter than "A decision was reached by the assembly to postpone the vote."

5. Try to avoid long sentences. A rough guideline is to avoid sentences longer than 40 words. It is usually more clear to break long sentences into 2 shorter sentences. Short sentences are useful to make important points or conclusions. Example: "This drug causes renal failure."

6. Use parallel constructions. When you have a series of words, phrases and clauses, they should be put in a parallel or similar form. This allows the reader to identify the relationship between them more clearly.

   Example: "In dealing with appendicitis, we learned that it is important to be aware of the symptoms, to know the physical findings, and to reexamine the patient frequently." This sentence has good parallel construction.

   In contrast: "In dealing with appendicitis, we learned that it is important to be aware of the symptoms, knowing the physical findings is important, and one should reexamine the patient frequently." is much less clear.

Another example: "Good surgical practice involves careful listening and clear decision making." is better than "Good surgical practice involves careful listening and the ability to make clear decisions."

7. Avoid long strings of nouns.

   Example: "This report explains our projects to stimulate improvements in medical education." is better than "This report explains our medical education improvement projects."

8. Use the verb form in preference to the noun form. Example: "The operation was performed successfully" is better than "The performance of the operation was a success."

9. Avoid multiple negatives. Example: "Less attention is paid to roentgenograms that lack clarity than to other kinds of images." is unclear. Better is: "Physicians pay more attention to images that are clear than to unclear images."

These rules are rough guidelines that may help you write better sentences. If this material is too elementary for this audience, never fear.

Improving your Writing: Paragraph Structure

What is a paragraph? It is a group of related sentences dealing with a single topic. Effective paragraphs have a topic sentence, unity, coherence, and good development. Let's look at each of these in turn.

The topic sentence explains the topic of the paragraph and it is usually best to place this sentence at or near the beginning of the paragraph. A good paragraph has unity, which means that it deals only with one subject and does not wander from topic to topic.

Coherence in a paragraph is related to unity and refers to the bridges or links between sentences. These links may be logical or verbal. Logical links carry the same idea from sentence to sentence. The use of parallel sentences is also a logical bridge.

Verbal links can be made by repeating a key word or phrase in each sentence. In addition, synonyms can be used in each sentence to link them together. Pronouns can also be used in one sentence referring to a word in another sentence in order to link 2 sentences together in the same paragraph.

Example: "When clinical trials give negative results, they will be considered failures until some other research group tries them again. Those that give a successful result in the treatment of the patient are the most rewarding." The pronouns in this paragraph that connect the sentences are "they" and "those."

Development of a paragraph means that the paragraph discusses completely the central idea. Good development can be made by using examples, citing data (statistics or results), citing testimony, using a story or anecdote, defining terms, examining etiology or causes, offering a chronology, making comparisons, or contrasting ideas. One way to develop a paragraph is to go from general to specific topics. Another way is to present ideas and events in a chronological manner.

How long should paragraphs be? Various papers have suggested anywhere from 3-5 sentences or sometimes more. Another guideline is 2-3 paragraphs per page.

The Format of a Paragraph

It is easier to read paragraphs if there is a blank line between them and if the first line of a paragraph is indented. These things make it easier for the eye to find the beginning of the paragraph and save the reader time and effort. Paragraphs are also easier to read if the right margin is irregular. However, the instructions to the author of various journals may require other formats.

Paragraph Transition

It is useful to use transition words and sentences to help the reader see the relationship between paragraphs. There are several ways to do this. One way is to tell the reader at the end of a paragraph about the next. Example: "This idea is discussed in more detail in the next few paragraphs." Another method is to use a word or phrase in the last sentence of a paragraph and then repeating it in the first sentence of the next paragraph. Also, one may use subject headings between paragraphs to announce that there is a change in subject. Example: "Paragraph Transition" shown above announces that there is a change in the topic. One may also place a single sentence paragraph between 2 larger paragraphs to link them.

Make it Concise!

After you have written your first draft and edited it at least once, it is important to make the paper short and concise. Scientists have a tendency to allow long expressions and unnecessary words to creep into their writing. This probably occurs because this is the way that we talk. We use extra words to fill in the space between our ideas. Editors do not like this for several reasons. One is that more print takes up more space and increases their costs. In addition, they want to publish as many good quality papers as they can in their allotted space. In the instructions to authors of many journals you will find limitations on abstract or manuscript size. Also, it is not uncommon to receive a paper back from a journal after review with the comment, "Please shorten this manuscript considerably before resubmitting."

The best way to do this is to go through the manuscript word-by-word and line-by-line and attempt to remove excess words. In spoken English, there are many words which act as fillers and can be removed in written papers.

For example, in the list below only the first word is necessary.

Check up on...
Green in color...
Small in size...
Few in number...
All of...
Refer back...

Another example is the use of "It ... that" phrases.

It would appear that... CAN BE REPLACED WITH Apparently...

In light of the fact that... CAN BE REPLACED WITH Because...

All redundancy, verbosity, and jargon should be removed from your paper. These 3 things tend to occur together. All pointless words must be removed.

REPLACE "in most cases" WITH "usually."

EXAMPLE: Due to the fact that transesophageal echocardiograms in most cases are performed in the hospital...

REPLACE WITH: Because transesophageal echocardiograms are usually done in the hospital...

Another way to shorten your text is to replace phrases with adjectives.

EXAMPLE: The left atrium, 45 mm in width,...

REPLACE WITH: The 45-mm wide left atrium ... OR The left atrium, 45 mm wide, ...

You can also replace "that" and "which" phrases.

EXAMPLE: The connection that Marrero (1999) found... COULD BE: The connection Marrero (1999) found

EXAMPLE: A pig with three legs that can fly ... COULD BE: A three-legged flying pig. (Perhaps not a very common example).

Many such examples can occur in a single paper and when

they are all corrected, the paper becomes considerably shorter and tighter. There are some scientific writers who believe that using long and wordy sentences makes them sound more intelligent and impressive. This is not true, and this tendency must be resisted.

In English, nouns can be used to modify or describe nouns. For example, "renal disease" can also be written as "kidney disease." When 2 or more nouns are placed together, this is called a "two-noun cluster." This is fine, but the use of more than 2 nouns together can be very confusing because it is not clear which noun is modifying which other noun. In this case it is better to make the text a little longer by using phrases so that the meaning is clear.

EXAMPLE: "infected dog cardiac samples" could have many different meanings. It is better to include a phrase to clarify the meaning, such as "cardiac samples from infected dogs" even though this is longer.

Use of the above points will make your papers more concise and readable.

Common Problems with Writing

1. Overuse of the Passive Voice

   The term active voice means that someone or something in the sentence does the action of the verb.

   Active voice: Dr. Thomas performed the operation.
   Passive voice: The operation was performed by Dr. Thomas.

Active voice gives energy to your writing. The use of the passive voice slows it down. The active voice is also 20-30% shorter. However, its use is very popular in scientific writing for several reasons. Some myths that promote the use of the passive voice are: The active voice is self-promoting. The scientist should stay out of the work. Use of the passive voice makes the writer less accountable. These are poor reasons to use the passive voice.

The passive voice is useful, however, when the doer of the action is unknown. Example: The patient was brought to the hospital. It is useful that the doer should remain unnamed. It is also useful when the receiver of the action is more important than the doer. Example: Dr. Williams was named Dean of the Medical School.

2. Use of Long Sentences

This is a mistake that I see very commonly in writing by non-native English speakers. Medicine and science are complicated enough without making it more difficult to understand with very long sentences. The meaning of the sentence can become lost. It is a mistake to try to put more than 2 ideas into a single sentence, but I have seen authors try to put up to 4 ideas in a single sentence. I believe short sentences are better even for native English speakers, because they make a scientific paper easier to read and more clear.

3. Wordiness

This refers to the use of long or complicated words when a simple and clear word would do just as well.

This can be avoided when the writer keeps in mind that he is writing to communicate and not to impress. Avoid the use of pompous or pretentious language. It is best to use specific nouns and strong verbs instead of a list of adjectives. Try to eliminate excessive words.

Do not use words together that mean the same thing. Example: A non-curative, palliative operation.

Certain phrases can be replaced by one word:
A limited number = one
A sizable percentage of = many
In the very near future = soon
To a large extent = largely
To a certain extent = in part
In the event that = if

4. Misused Words

Example: The patients were tested utilizing exercise echocardiography.
The word "using" should be used here. Utilize implies a new use for something.

Example: Penicillin can affect a cure.

The words "affect" and "effect" are commonly confused. Keep in mind the following definitions.

Affect (verb) = to influence
Affect (noun) = behavior, outward appearance
Effect (verb) = to bring about
Effect (noun) = outcome

The abbreviation i.e. is often used mistakenly in place of egg. E.g. means "exempli gratia" in Latin or "for example" in English. I.e. means "id est" in Latin or "that is" in English. I.e. is used before amplifications of what has previously been written.

Punctuation in Scientific Writing

It is always best to keep thing simple. For example, if you are writing a sentence with many punctuation marks and you are not sure if it is correct, rewrite the sentence to make it simpler or break the sentence into 2 separate sentences. Of course a period is required at the end of every sentence. It is probably better to avoid using a semicolon (;) in the middle of a sentence and to break the sentence into 2 instead. If you write something and then find that it is not clear, break it into several sentences for increased clarity.

The comma (,) has a wide variety of uses: it can separate, link, or enclose. It can add emphasis or clarity to a sentence. A dependent clause at the beginning of a sentence requires a comma to separate it from the main part of the sentence. Clauses in the middle of a sentence should be enclosed by commas if they change the meaning of the sentence. Clauses that use "which" generally need a comma.

When giving a series of items it is useful to include a comma before the "and" as well as between each item. This increases clarity.

Example: The analysis revealed the presence of normal amounts of calcium, potassium, and chloride.

For long complex sentences, you can also use semicolons and numbers to punctuate them.

Example: All patients (1) were younger than 18; (2) had underlying heart disease of some kind; and (3) were survivors of sudden cardiac death.

Quotation marks should be used for direct quotations, titles of articles, and for terms used in a novel way.

Example: The article, "Effect of digoxin on atrial fibrillation" was published in the Journal of Unreliable Results.

Example: The term "angina" was used for throat pain in the past.

Hyphens: There is a lot of confusion about when to use hyphens.

Several rules may be helpful.

1. Use a hyphen for fractions or ratios that are adjectives. Three-to-one vote, or one-half removed.
2. In compound numbers. Twenty-one to ninety-nine.
3. To reduce redundancy. Second- or third-generation immigrants were better adapted.
4. With letter or number modifiers. 50-year old man, A-bomb.
5. With a prefix of a word that is a proper noun. Pre-Einstein physics.
6. When the same vowel ends the prefix and begins the word. Pre-existing or anti-inflammatory.
7. To create compound modifiers. Eight-sided crystal, lipid-bearing capsule.
8. To avoid ambiguity. Re-cover the dish so that the bacteria can recover.

Punctuation

Overall the best approach to using punctuation is to keep things simple. If you create a complex sentence and you are not sure if the punctuation that you have used is correct, then you have probably written a sentence that would confuse your readers also. Punctuation should add clarity to your writing and not detract from it. In order to accomplish this, often it is best to break up long complex sentences into several smaller ones.

Sentences, which join 2 clauses or ideas together, can benefit from the use of punctuation to clarify their meaning.

Example: Although I.V. nitroglycerin was discontinued after 9 days the chest pain stopped.

The meaning of this sentence is not clear. It could be written in 2 different ways with differing meanings: Although I.V. nitroglycerin was discontinued after 9 days, the chest pain stopped. OR Although I.V. nitroglycerin was discontinued, after 9 days the chest pain stopped.

The comma (,) can be used in several ways: to link, enclose, separate, or show omissions. If a dependent clause comes before a sentence, it needs a comma. The prior sentence is an example of this. If a clause occurs in the middle of a sentence, you must determine if it is essential to the meaning of the sentence. If so, then no commas should be used. This means that clauses with "which" but not "that" require commas.

Commas are used to set off a series or list of items in a sentence.

Example: Chest pain may be caused by ischemia, pericarditis, and pleuritis.

However, when the items on the list are complex and have their own punctuation, it is better to use semicolons (;) or numbers in parenthesis to separate the items.

Confusing example: The criteria stated that patients with left atrial enlargement greater than 6 cm were included, but those with mitral stenosis were not, the patient had to be older than 65 years and no patient with chest wall abnormalities, prior cardiac surgery, or a prior myocardial infarction was included.

Better example: All patients (1) exhibited left atrial

enlargement greater than 6 cm on echocardiogram but without mitral stenosis; (2) were older than 65; (3) had no chest wall abnormality, prior myocardial infarction or prior cardiac surgery.

Quotation marks (" ")

These are used for direct quotations, titles of articles of book chapters, and to emphasize selected words. If you use the exact words of another author or speaker, you should use quotation marks.

Example: An article, "Effects of Ramipril on Systolic Blood Pressure in Ischemic Heart Disease" was recently published in Circulation. The authors stated, "Ramipril was associated with a low incidence of adverse reactions." It was not clear what they meant by "low incidence."

Note that in the last example, the comma appeared inside the quotation marks. In American style, commas and periods always appear inside the quotation marks. In the United Kingdom, punctuation is placed outside the quotation marks unless it is part of the quote.

It is also possible to set off long quotes as a separate paragraph, which is indented about 1 cm from the left margin.

Example: Buckingham and Kennedy (1986) wrote:

The signal-averaged electrocardiogram shows promise as a diagnostic test for the prediction of ventricular tachycardia but not

for ventricular fibrillation. Further studies
are required to elucidate the mechanisms
of...

I am also showing the use of another punctuation mark, the ellipsis (...). This is used to mark missing words, an uncertain pause, or an abrupt interruption. Note that only 3 points are used. The use of more points is discouraged and appears exaggerated.

Formatting Your Paper

Some Formatting Issues

As you prepare your second draft, a number of issues will come up. By this time your paper has its basic organization and you have put it aside long enough so that you can look at it from a fresh viewpoint. Now it is time to start preparing its format. Format includes its organization, general appearance and the manner in which you present your data. This is where you will have to consult the instructions to authors of your chosen journal and follow them closely. It is also valuable to read several papers in the chosen journal so that you will know what papers published in this journal look like.

Can you use a computer program to format your paper for your chosen journal? Unfortunately, although word-processing software and other products can be very helpful, you cannot rely on them to completely format your paper. The most efficient way to produce a scientific paper is to learn how to write papers yourself or to use the services of a professional editor. This requires that you read and write many papers. Computer programs contain grammar-checking software. I am writing this book with Microsoft Word and I have used their grammar and spell checking software to check this book and many other papers. However, this program and others like it have important limitations and require the author's interaction when they are used. The best time to use this software is towards the end of writing your paper. Then they can be used to catch errors. Unfortunately, you cannot rely on such programs to produce understandable well-written scientific English. There is no substitute for long experience in reading and writing scientific papers.

Specific formatting issues

We can now deal with a number of specific formatting issues such as capitalization, use of foreign words and phrases, punctuation, abbreviations, number formatting, etc.

Foreign words and phrases

Some foreign words and phrases have been more or less completely assimilated into the English language and require no special treatment. Phrases not completely assimilated should be italicized (for example, *sine qua non, idee fixe*). In general it is better not to use foreign phrases that have not been assimilated into English unless necessary. Examples of phrases that have been assimilated include "memorandum" and "formula." There are some Latin phrases used in writing and it is generally preferable to use the English equivalent. For "viz.", substitute "namely" and for "circa" substitute "about." The use of i.e. (id est = that is), e.g. (exempli gratia = for example) and et al. (et alii = and others) is still common and acceptable. Certain Latin phrases should always follow the noun that they describe. For example (in vivo = in the living body) should be written "tests *in vivo*" and not "*in vivo* tests." Also, "*in vivo*" should be italicized. Other phrases in this category include (*in vitro*, in an artificial environment), (*de novo* = anew) and (*in vacuo* = in the absence of air). The plurals of Latin word can be confusing. Words ending in "a" have an "e" at the end when plural and those ending in "um" add an "a" at the end when plural. Examples: datum and data, larva and larvae.

Acknowledgements

An acknowledgement can and should be used to mention someone or an organization that contributed to the work of your paper but whose contribution does not merit authorship. This could include general support of your department chairman, or financial or technical support. An acknowledgement can also be used to mention financial relationships that may pose a conflict of interest. When someone has contributed to your paper and you wish to mention him or her, you should also mention their contribution or function (i.e. scientific advisor, critical review of the study proposal, data collection, participants in a multicenter trial, etc.).

It is important to get the consent of those who you include in an acknowledgement for several reasons. It is possible that they may not agree with what you have written in your paper and readers of the paper will infer that they have endorsed the contents. Also, it is possible that someone may be offended by the way that you acknowledge him or her and once this is published, it will be impossible to undo it.

Abbreviations, Acronyms and Others

An abbreviation saves space and time in a scientific manuscript, but must be used correctly to be effective. An abbreviation is a shortened form of the complete word (e.g. avg., temp.). Acronyms are formed from the initial letters of a series of words in a phrase and are written in capital letters (e.g. ELISA, DNA, NIH, etc.). Periods are included with abbreviations but not with acronyms. However, the use of periods with abbreviations is slowly dying out, so you will have to check the instructions to authors for your target journal to find out what is required. In either case, it is important to define an abbreviation both the first time it is used in the abstract and in the text of the paper.

Example: Be sure to consult the instructions to authors (ITA) of your target journal.

You should avoid using multiple abbreviations in one sentence or close together in the text of your paper. This makes the text very difficult to read.

Example:
Incorrect: Use of IV BCG has a LD50 toxicity of ...

To make an abbreviation or acronym plural, add a small s. Do not use an apostrophe.

Example:
Correct: In the early 1980s, WBCs ...
Incorrect: In the early 1980's, WBC's ...

Many words have approved abbreviations, which should always be used. Some of these lists can be found in style manuals (see http://www.lifescipub.com/books.htm). Specific fields of science have their own approved abbreviations, which are published in various places. These may be given in the ITA or at least the ITA may provide a reference where they can be found. (Note that I defined ITA earlier in the text).

Do not include abbreviations in the title of your paper and do not begin a sentence with one. Needless to say, you should be consistent and use the same abbreviation for a word throughout your paper. If you are in doubt about the correct abbreviation for a term, do not abbreviate, spell out the word or phrase normally.

Bibliographies

The required format for each journal can be found in their instructions to authors (ITA). This is usually found in a copy of the journal or on their web page. The use of computer software to manage your bibliography can save you valuable time and help avoid errors in formatting. A little known fact is that some journal editors look at your bibliography carefully. If it is formatted improperly and contains many errors, they assume that you scientific work suffers from the same problems (i.e. that you scientific work has many errors). Typically, good bibliographic software allows you to reformat all of your references to meet the requirements of any given journal. This saves you the trouble of doing this manually if you need to resubmit the paper to a second journal. The software will also number your references and put your bibliography in correct order and add the citations to the text. The software can import your references from the Internet services like PubMed or Medline so that you do not have to type them all by hand. In addition to helping you with your papers, this type of software can help you track the literature in a certain field and organize your collection of papers. There are online versions of this software as well as software programs that can be purchased and installed on your computer.

See the Wikipedia comparison of these software packages:

https://en.wikipedia.org/wiki/Comparison_of_reference_management_software

Reporting of Numerical Data

Presentation of Numerical Data

The successful and clear presentation of numerical data is essential to almost all scientific papers. Numerical data can be presented in a number of ways, including text, statistics, graphs, and tables. In this article we will focus on the proper presentation in text and in later articles we will cover other methods. The use of all of these techniques in proper balance with each other is important.

While you are preparing your paper, you should be organizing your data as you collect it. The exact way that you organize it will depend on your field and on your own preferences. Some authors will wait until they start writing the paper to develop tables and figures while others do it along the way. In general, it is better to start this process early so that your visual aids can be effectively integrated into your presentation.

This section will cover the use of tables and other sections will deal with graphs, photographs, and other visual aids. It is important that you select those visual aids, which are most effective in presenting your ideas and which work well together with each other and the text of your paper. Although they are widely used, it is not mandatory to include a table in every scientific paper. Sometimes tables and other visual aids look similar. When an editor looks at your paper, if a visual aid is not a table, it is a figure.

You should use the visual aids most appropriate for your audience. Examine your target journal carefully and try to mimic its style. Also, pay close attention to the instructions to authors regarding the use of tables and figures. Do not duplicate data in the table and in the text. You should also refer to each table at least once in the text of your paper when most relevant.

Numbers in Text

It is always better to use numbers instead of vague adjectives to describe data. For example, "in 5 seconds" is much better than "very quickly." Numbers contribute to the precision of scientific data and are therefore essential. Numbers in text should be expressed in a consistent manner. The exact format required varies from journal to journal and you must check the instructions to authors to find out the preference of your target journal. Some journals require you to spell out all small numbers less than 10. There is a trend for an increasing number of journals to use Arabic numbers throughout in order to save printing costs.

In general you must spell out numbers that begin a sentence.

Example: "Twenty rats were then removed from the cage." However, it is often better to try to rewrite the sentence to that it does not start with a number. "Then, 20 rats were removed from the cage." When two numbers appear together, one must be spelled out to avoid confusion. Example: "3 15-ml aliquots were added..." should be written as "Three 15-ml aliquots were added..." When designating something with a definite unit of measurement, Arabic numbers can be used. Example: "5.5 m" or "38.6 °C." SI units should be used whenever possible. SI means 'Systeme International d'Unites' and is an international system designed to correct confusion in the metric system. In general, Arabic numbers are better than Roman numbers because they are easier to read and interpret.

When reporting percentages, always include Arabic numbers before the % sign. Be aware of the different definition of "percentile" which is a statistical term for the value in a distribution of frequencies divided into 100 equal groups. When presenting percentage data, give the exact number of subjects if less than 50 and do not report decimal percentages (20.5%) unless you have more than 1000 subjects. Example: "Anthrax was found in 50% (18) of the animals."

Likewise, equations must be expressed clearly. Simple equations can be included in the text: i.e. $x = 10y + 9$. More complicated equations need to be set off from text by triple spacing. When presenting a series of equations identify them with a number in parenthesis, which is placed at the left or the right margin. Also line them up so that the equals sign (=) are on top of each other.

$$f(y) = (3x + 4z)(a) \qquad\qquad (1)$$
$$P(x,y) = \cos(x - z) \qquad\qquad (2)$$

To show division, it is better to use "/" instead of placing part of the formula over a line. This makes the formatting and typesetting easier.

The Use of Tables

While writing your first draft, at some point you must decide whether to put your data into tables, graphs or the text. Tables are useful for presenting precise numerical data, large amounts of data or large numbers, summarizing information, and presenting complex information. In any case you must review the instructions to authors to find out what kinds of tables and how many are allowed per article in your target journal. These instructions may specify the numbers of tables allowed and their formats. One useful rule of thumb is that there should be no more than one table or illustration per 1000 words of text. Therefore one approach would be to first determine how many tables you will use. After this you can then select which information is most appropriate to present in tabular format.

There is a difference in the tables used for short oral presentations and those used for publications. Tables presented as part of a slideshow are usually smaller and simpler. Publication allows for more complex tables. Tables should not be used if the data can be summarized in the text easily. Tables should also not be used when the data can be shown more clearly in a graph. Tables can be used to list text information such as a list of symptoms or physical findings.

Tables can be quite variable. Some contain text information while others are numerical. They can be simple and small or they can be complex and span several pages. Tables consist of a title at the top and are usually numbered (table 1, table 2, etc.). They have several column headings collectively called the "box heading" and several row headings collectively called the "stub."

A well-designed table can help the reader see patterns and relationships in your data and is the most efficient way to present exact numerical data. Tables should not be used to present all of your data, but should be used for data central to the message of your paper. Tables used for slide presentations should be small and simple whereas tables in a publication can be larger and more complex if necessary.

Tables are more difficult and expensive to typeset and editors will ask you to remove them if they are unnecessary. There is a tendency to overuse tables. Before submitting your paper to the journal, look at the tables carefully to see if some can be eliminated or combined. You cannot include all of your numerical data just because you went to a lot of trouble to collect it. Each table should be an independent, important and indispensable part of your paper. When referring to your table in the text, state why the tabular information is needed. Example: "Affected patients had higher systolic blood pressure (Table 1)" is much better than "The results are shown in Table 1." Do not write "shown in the table above (or below)" because you do not know where the table will be placed in the paper. When you have several tables, you must place them in proper, logical sequence. They must also be mentioned in the text of the paper in the same order. In addition, try to make the appearance and form of the tables consistent to allow the reader to compare the tables. This can be done by using the same or similar format and the same headings.

Each table must be organized. The row and column headings must be arranged in a logical order. Include units of measurement in column headings (SI metric system). It is useful to report sample sizes ("n = 230") in tables. Fill all cells in the field. Use "ND" for not done and "NA" for not applicable. Do not use dashes, as they are less clear. Round off numbers and percentages to avoid pseudo-accuracy. The numbers in the same column should be given to the same level of accuracy. Experiment with the table format (for example, change the rows to columns if the table is too wide).

Biomedical Statistics

A quick look at almost any medical paper today will show the use of statistics in the description of the methods and results. Most papers will quote a "p value" to support a level of "significance." In addition, many papers include multivariate analyses of complex data sets.

I often see statistical terms misused in such a way that indicates the writer does not understand the basic concepts underlying statistics. It is essential that those involved in biomedical research and writing understand the basic concepts and definitions in this field. They must be able to read the results of others intelligently and be able to include the same terms in their own papers. The necessary information can be obtained in a short course on statistics, which is offered at many universities, or from basic textbooks on the subject (see below). This article will not be able to adequately cover all of these subjects. In addition, for complex analyses, it is wise for the medical writer to involve a statistical consultant for the analysis of the data. The inclusion of a trained statistician as one of the authors of a scientific paper can be easily justified and is actually looked upon with favor by journal editors and reviewers. However, when a statistician analyzes data from a medical study, it is necessary for him to have some understanding of the related medical knowledge of the subject at hand. This allows him to better interpret the results and to suggest further avenues of statistical analysis.

For simple data sets, many researchers prefer to perform their own analysis using off-the-shelf statistical software. Many researchers have a sufficient background in statistics to undertake a more sophisticated analysis. Some medical journals are now requiring a separate statistical review when complex statistical results are presented.

It is important for the researcher to understand the concepts of random variables, probability distributions, and the standard notation used to describe statistical analysis and results. Medical writers and researchers should know, for example, when it is appropriate to use parametric and nonparametric methods. A complete discussion of this question is beyond the scope of this article, but parametric methods can be used with continuous variables if they are normally distributed.

Another important concept is that of sample size. There can be many problems with the statistical analysis of a small sample size. In clinical trials, a sample size with adequate power can be calculated or estimated before the trial begins, which aids in planning the trial. In order to do this, however, the researcher must know or be able to estimate the variability of the data (i.e. the standard deviation) and the difference that he is trying to detect (e.g. 10 percent). Sometimes these values cannot be known in advance of a full-scale clinical trial and a pilot study must be done to estimate them. In addition, a larger sample size will allow detection of smaller differences between 2 populations. Of course, larger sample sizes may be impractical due to cost or other factors. The calculation of a sample size may in fact show that a given clinical trial cannot be done at all because the sample size required is too large.

Another basic concept that is sometimes confused is the relative importance of statistical significance and clinical significance. A result from a study may be statistically significant but have no practical clinical meaning. Of course, the medical researcher is searching for results that are both statistically and clinically significant.

Books on basic statistics

Biometry: The Principles and Practice of Statistics in Biological Research
Sokal and Rohlf. 1994, W H Freeman & Co

How to Report Statistics in Medicine: Annotated Guidelines for Authors, Editors, and Reviewers
by Lang and Secic. 1997, American College of Physicians.

Use of Figures in your Paper

While you are doing your study, you should be organizing your data as you collect it. Some authors will wait until they start writing the paper to develop tables and figures while others do it along the way. In general, it is better to start this process early so that your visual aids can be effectively integrated into your presentation. The correct preparation of the many types of figures is a large subject and is difficult to cover here completely.

In this section we will deal with graphs, photographs, and other visual aids. When an editor looks at your paper, if a visual aid is not a table, it is a figure. It is important that you select those visual aids, which are most effective in presenting your ideas and which work well together with each other and the text of your paper. Although they are widely used, it is not mandatory to include a figure in every scientific paper.

Examine your target journal carefully and try to copy its style with respect to the use of figures and tables. Also, pay close attention to the instructions to authors regarding the use of figures. These instructions will tell you how many copies to send, whether original photos or copies are acceptable, etc. They may also tell you how many figures or tables are allowed.

There are many kinds of figures but they can be divided into 3 types: numerical (bar graphs, pie charts, etc.), explanatory (diagrams, etc.), and documents (photos, machine printouts, etc.). Whenever possible try to combine figures for efficiency. Figures used in spoken talks tend to be simpler than those in papers. If you are using figures from a slide presentation, quite often 2 or more can be combined in a paper.

The figure should be independent of the text. This means that it should have all the symbols and abbreviations defined in the figure legend so that the figure can be understood separately. At the same time, the figure must work together with the text to describe an object, a process, or a concept.

You should refer to each figure at least once in the text of your paper when most relevant. Do not duplicate data in a table, the text and in a figure. Readers tend to look at your figures first. Small things can make a difference in how a figure looks (i.e. size of lettering). You may wish to use a professional to help prepare your illustrations.

There are many computer programs available now that can be used to prepare figures. You must pay close attention to size and scale because when figures are reduced, the text may become illegible or other flaws may be exaggerated. A rectangle with a vertical size of 2 to a horizontal size of 3 is a good ratio with a pleasing appearance.

Figure legends are important and must be written carefully. Legends should explain the meaning of each figure, differentiate them from other figures in the paper and at the same time be concise.

Use a graph instead of a table to present numerical data when you believe that it will present the data in a manner more understandable to your reader. Graphs can also be used to emphasize relationships between variables. When using a computer to create one, first create several different types of graphs from the same data to see which one is the best. Then, modify the fonts, type size, symbols, shading, etc. to make the most legible figure possible.

Figures can be used to present data that would otherwise appear in a table, especially if you want to emphasize relationships within that data. However, as mentioned previously, you should not present the same data in both. There are several types of graphs that can be used to present such data: line graphs, bar graphs, pie charts, and others. Line graphs are probably the most commonly used type of graph in scientific writing. They show continuous variables and may demonstrate trends or movements over time. They range from simple representations of results to complex statistical analysis. However, they are more difficult to understand than bar graphs. When using a line graph, it is important to keep them simple, to distinguish different variables with different symbols and to label each line. A clear and detailed legend is also necessary.

Logarithmic graphs are similar but use a logarithmic scale. This is usually done to compare data where the rate of change is more important than the quantity of change. These graphs are also complicated and require more care in their construction and more explanation in the text. Another type of graph is the scattergraph, which shows a series of unconnected dots between variables. They can be used to show a relationship and sometimes a line is drawn through the dots to show this relationship. At other times they are used to show that there is no relationship between variables. They can also be plotted on logarithmic scales and require more explanation in the text than other types of graphs.

Bar graphs are simple to make and to understand. They can show data without implying a relationship. The bars can be horizontal or vertical but should be laid out in the way that the reader expects. When showing cause and effect data, it is better to use the horizontal axis for the independent variable and the vertical axis for the dependent variable. Bar graphs are best when presenting data to general audiences.

Pie charts are popular and used often. However, it is difficult to visually compare the areas in the chart. They are useful to attract attention and when comparing 5 or fewer items.

With any of the above types of charts, it is important for the author to present the data accurately and not to try to mislead the reader. Graphs can be distorted in many different ways and journal editors are likely to notice. For example, manipulation of the scale, deletion of data points, or enlargement of data points so that any line would pass through them are all possible abuses. As emphasized previously, it is important to only use figures when necessary.

Documentary illustrations include photographs such as x-rays or roentgenograms. When making photographs, it is best to make many, both in color and in black and white, and then select the best for your paper. These photos should be well focused and not have cluttered backgrounds. Color photos should be used only when the color is necessary. The photo must be cropped to show the most interesting finding and may require labeling with letters or symbols. This requires careful attention to detail.

Chapter 3. The Journal Article and Publication Strategy

Writing manuscripts for scientific journals is a very important task of the medical writer. For many medical writers this will represent the most important part of their work. Successful publication of research findings in a medical journal is an important recognition of the quality of the work and its author. Research published in primary journals is valued by the scientific community. Scientists seek to publish their findings for professional recognition and to spread scientific knowledge.

Publication of papers in scientific journals requires several different skills. The writer will be challenged to be a manager and a diplomat, as well as a good writer. The writer may need to involve experts in other fields to help him. For example, if the writer is not an expert on statistics he may wish to include a statistician in the work. Learning to write papers for biomedical journals is a difficult and challenging. The medical writer must commit himself to learning how to publish papers in scientific and medical journals. Primary journals publish papers that are the first public dissemination of a study. Almost always, peer-review is required before papers are accepted.

The specific requirements of scientific journals vary widely but the acronym "IMRAD" summarizes a standard that is common.

I = introduction
M = methods
R = results
A = and
D = discussion

Typically these papers are short, for example 4-11 pages and there may be specific requirements for text, tables, figures, and references, which all must be carefully followed. It is important to examine the target journal carefully to see how papers are prepared for this journal. Sections not identified by the IMRAD acronym include title, abstract, acknowledgments, and references. The International Committee of Medical Journal Editors has published the Uniform Requirements for Manuscripts Submitted to Biomedical Journals, a document that is periodically updated and which has been adopted by many journals as part of their guidelines. This document contains a lot of very useful information for the medical writer.

The following is the sequence of steps to follow in preparing a medical paper.

Step by step approach to writing a paper
Decide on the message of the paper.
Decide if it is worth writing.
Choose the audience.
Select the journal and look up their requirements.
Search the literature on this subject.
Choose format: research paper, case report, review, opinion paper.
Prepare an outline.
Write the first draft.
Make revisions.
Prepare the submission letter.
Submit.
Respond to editor's decision.

Why are Journal Articles Rejected?

We can begin by analyzing which journal articles are accepted or rejected for publication and why. This will give us insights into how to write a successful paper. Below are the three most common reasons that articles are rejected by medical and scientific journals.

1. The manuscript is not appropriate for the chosen journal.
2. The manuscript describes a poorly designed or poorly conducted study.
3. The manuscript is poorly written.

We will discuss each of these in turn. The fact that many editors receive manuscripts that they consider inappropriate for their journals indicates that the authors are not doing their homework. The selection of the best journal for your manuscript is very important. One logical place to start is the Information for Authors page that is contained in every journal. This information, sometimes called "Instructions for Authors", can usually be found on the Internet.

The journal author page contains useful information for each journal, including the journal's mission statement, the types of articles that it accepts, a description of the journal's readers, the manuscript format, and specific instructions. Careful reading of this page helps authors determine if their paper is appropriate for that particular journal. In addition, the author should have read the journal before and be familiar with its contents and format.

Not Appropriate for the Chosen Journal

Not every paper is appropriate for the best journals, (i.e. the New England Journal of Medicine). The top journals have a higher rejection rate and are very competitive. It is best to try to match the quality of your paper to the level of the journal to give yourself a good chance of acceptance. This topic is discussed in more detail later in this book. Save you best work for the best journals. It is usually not possible to publish your first paper in the best journal.

Poorly Designed or Conducted Studies

Common problems here include insufficient information, inadequate or inappropriate samples, biased samples, confounding factors, unclear endpoints, or unclear hypothesis. These problems must be avoided from the very beginning of the conduct of the study and they cannot be corrected even by expert medical editing.

Poorly Written Manuscript

Editors and reviewers commonly tell me that they sometimes receive a manuscript that is so full of errors that it cannot be evaluated. More commonly, manuscripts may contain errors in grammar or style that distract the reviewer's attention from the essential scientific message of the paper. More importantly, they can create the impression that because the author has made grammatical errors, his scientific work also contains errors.

Papers written by authors whose native language is not

English can benefit from professional editing by an editing service. Sometimes you can find a colleague to do this for you. Otherwise please consult a professional editing service.

There is also scientific data that suggests that poorly written papers or papers from authors whose native language is not English, may be at a disadvantage. Coates et al surveyed 120 articles submitted to Cardiovascular Research and found clear indications that careless writing could have either a direct or subliminal influence on whether a paper was accepted or rejected. On equal scientific merit, a badly written article had less chance of being accepted.

First Impressions are Important

When a journal editor receives a paper, he or she normally sends it out to at least 2 reviewers who then judge it to see if it is good enough for that particular journal. After several weeks, the reviewers (also called referees) send it back to the editor with their comments and evaluation. The comments are then sent back to the author along with the editor's decision whether to accept, accept with revisions, or reject the paper. The evaluation is kept confidential, but the editor uses it to decide whether or not to accept the article. The editor may reject the paper, accept it, or send it back to the authors to be revised according to the comments of the reviewers, whose names are never revealed. The author must then revise it and resubmit it. It is then typically sent back to the same reviewers for review again. This entire process may be repeated for one or more cycles. Articles are very seldom accepted in their original state; they are either rejected or accepted subject to revision.

If an article is submitted to a journal that is poorly written (for example, in poor English), this makes a poor initial impression and even if this error is corrected later, the chances that the paper will be accepted by that journal are reduced. Some editors also look carefully at the bibliography. If it is poorly formatted, with numerous mistakes and typographical errors, they may take this as a sign that the scientific work in the main body of the paper was likewise poorly done. This may not be true, but unfortunately, this is the impression that is created. It is a mistake to think that the bibliography is not an important part of the paper.

Therefore, it is best to make a good impression from the beginning. You would not go to an important business meeting poorly dressed, and the same principle applies in this case. If the editor requesting that the English or some other problem be corrected and sends an article back to the author, this should, of course, be done before resubmission, however, it cannot be guaranteed that it will then be accepted. If the article is ultimately rejected by the initial journal, all is not lost. If the article has good scientific material and the format is correct, it can always be submitted to another journal for a fresh start with better chances for success. However, the authors should always use the feedback from the reviewers from the first journal to improve their article before submitting to a second journal. It is also possible that the second journal may select the same referee to review the article.

Some items to pay particular attention to in order to make a good first impression:

1. The paper should look well organized, with clear section headings. In particular, the title page must be well

organized and include all the necessary information, which is usually spelled out in the instructions to authors.

2. The paper should follow the Instructions to Authors for the intended journal.

3. The bibliography should be correctly formatted and without mistakes or omissions.

4. Obvious mistakes in English grammar and usage should be avoided.

5. The article should always include a cover letter. The Instructions to Authors for the intended journal will sometimes spell out language that must be contained in this letter. For example, the authors may be required to state that the article is not being simultaneously considered elsewhere or that they all agree to its submission, etc. The cover letter should state why you think this article will be relevant and interesting to the readers of the intended journal.

6. Pay careful attention to how other articles published in the intended journal have been formatted and try to mimic their format and style.

Publication Strategy

Physicians and scientists pursuing an academic career must follow a strategy to insure that many of their papers are published and that their reputation increases. This section on publication strategy is devoted to this theme.

Why is the journal acceptance rate so low? Among the papers submitted to ranking journals, 1/3 or less get mildly favorable reports. With 2 referees, the chance that a typical paper will get a favorable recommendation from both is about 11% (1/9).

Then what is the correct strategy to follow? There is no such thing as luck in publication. Hard and painstaking work, coupled with careful risk taking, is required for success. When you submit your paper, it will undergo peer review, normally by 2 reviewers. Please be aware that all referees are not equal. Comments of a well-known referee may count more. When you receive the comments from the referees, try to determine which referee is more important. When a paper is rejected, the editors paid more attention to the negative aspects of your paper. If you eliminate or reduce the negative elements, your paper is more likely to be accepted.

If your paper is not accepted, this may have several possible meanings. It may be due to a lack of experience. This can be remedied. You may need to submit more papers. Volume also increases the acceptance rate because of learning by doing. You need to identify the cause and act accordingly. There might be biases against you based on race, sex, nationality, or schooling. You may not be able to eliminate their biases, but you can avoid them.

You should diversify your research portfolio. If the average wait for an acceptance is 1 year and the average wait for rejection is 6 months, it is important to have several papers under review at all times. Remember that survival is more important than glory in the early stages of your career. Diversification of the research portfolio is particularly important during the first 5 years of your career when each publication counts heavily.

Other reasons to diversify your research portfolio include the following:

- If you have a solid hit in one area, then continue your effort to establish your name as an expert in that field before you move into another field.
- Writing several papers in a very narrow area is risky. It is like putting all your eggs in one basket.
- Continuing to write papers in the same narrow area without evidence of success is risky.
- Try to maintain papers under review at all times

If acceptance rate of the top ranking journals is 15%, you need 7 papers under review to get one paper accepted per year. If you want 10 papers accepted in the first 5 years of your career, you need about a dozen papers under review at all times. 6 papers should be under review at all times for untenured authors. However, this does *not* mean that you should write 7 new papers each year.

If you have 2 ideas should you put them in one paper? In general, no, separate them into 2 papers. Do not try to put down everything you know about a subject in one paper. One question is: What will you do next? Also, as a paper's length increases beyond 15 pages, the chance of acceptance shrinks. When a topic is appropriately split into two papers, the probability of getting at least one of them accepted more than doubles. You will also get a paper accepted sooner.

Short papers are better because:

- Editors like short papers.

- The chance that a referee will detect a mathematical error declines.
- Referees will return the report faster.
- The chance that a referee will misunderstand the paper also decreases.

You should also diversify the journals you approach. Sending all papers to top journals is risky. Sending all papers to low-quality journals is also unsatisfactory. You will regret it if all the papers are accepted! Your curriculum vitae should contain some publications in the top journals. The quantity of publications is also important. Having 3 papers in different journals is better than 3 in one journal, if the relative quality of the journals is the same.

Publication strategy: Writing

It is important to write clearly. The main assumptions and results should be explained clearly. If there are many assumptions, present them together in one place. Do not bury them in long paragraphs. Define every symbol when it is first introduced. Otherwise, the referees will be frustrated, and you won't get a favorable report. Clearly state the contributions of the paper in the concluding remarks.

Learning to use the appropriate software is useful in writing papers. (See the <u>software reviews</u> in this book). Be independent of secretaries. Word processing skills are particularly helpful when your revision is minor. Bibliographic software is very useful. Be aware that researchers without computer skills are an endangered species.

It is important to keep up with the current literature. Using key words, search if others have written papers on the same subjects. By not duplicating what others have done, you will save time and effort. Subscribe to a few specialized journals in your field. General journals are not cost effective as a source of research information. Use the library for other journals.

In order to stay updated you can subscribe to selected email newsletters. Many journals allow you to make an email subscription for their table of contents to be sent to you with each issue. You can also use a special storage feature on PubMed www. ncbi.nlm.nih.gov periodically to accomplish the same thing.

Present your papers at regional, national, or international conferences. You may get surprisingly valuable feedback. This is also an important way for you to become familiar with others working in the same area. Presenting papers within your own department is not effective.

Rejection

One gets rejection letters more often than not. Unfortunately, this is inevitable. You must develop a thick skin and be a good loser. This game is not for the faint-hearted. If you have a good paper, it needs at least 3 chances at ranking journals. If you ignore a paper more than one month, you are likely to lose interest. Do not allow this to happen.

There are probably about 100 experts in your field who are likely to be referees of your papers. Prepare a list of 100 experts in your main research areas. Try to meet them over a 5-year period. In order to do this present papers at, or at least attend, 2 professional meetings a year. When presenting papers or attending regional, national, or international meetings, try to get to know your colleagues and maintain contacts with them. However, do not send copies of your papers to them unless requested to do so. You will also need them later: they can write letters of recommendation when you seek promotion and tenure at your university.

Journal articles first

The useful life of a book is about 1 to 2 years. The life of a journal article is about 10 years. Publishers do not spend much money to advertise your book because profit margins are small. Book authors are alone and books do not go through the peer review process. Journal rankings are used to evaluate the quality of your research for academic promotion. The following weights should be used: 1 = an article in a good journal, 0.5 - 1 = a whole book, maybe 2 if it is very popular, 0.1 = a chapter in a book someone else edited. Textbooks usually do not count, however, handbooks and some special book series are better because of their long shelf life (10+ years).

Do not give away your precious idea for a paper as a chapter of a book, unless it is your specific desire to help others. First, publish your original idea in an article and then maybe in a book, not vice versa. Journals will not knowingly publish an article if the substance was published in a book previously.

Collaboration

Find seasoned coauthors with publication experience, work

together, and share the benefits. Acting alone is a risky strategy, especially for those just out of training. You have to become independent at some point, though. With seasoned coauthors, the probability of acceptance will likely more than double.

Through your coauthors, you may be introduced to an established group of investigators. You may also learn how to write better. It is best to divide up the work with coauthors ahead of time. Be considerate when determining the order of authors. For a long-term relationship, alternate the order of appearance, especially when the contributions are about the same. Another practical idea is to flip a coin.

You should be tolerant of your coauthors. Remember that the sum of the subjective contributions of coauthors always > 100%. Removing an inactive coauthor from the paper may not give you peace of mind, especially if it is done abruptly. Keep pace with your coauthors. If a coauthor does not contribute anything, caution must be exercised. Often the animosity generated by excluding him is not worth the gain.

Publication strategy: Avoid Dead Topics

If the most recent references related to your paper are 5 years old, then the subject that you are studying may be a dying issue. Editors are reluctant to accept such papers. In part, this is because it is difficult for the editor to find suitable referees for outdated topics.

Your inability to find sufficient references indicates one of two possibilities:

1. You have not read the literature.
2. Others are not interested in the topic; hence, it is unlikely to produce output.

The bulk of papers published today are modifications of the existing literature or tests of existing theories. However, something in the paper must be original because duplication is not an extension of knowledge. Therefore it is a good plan to extend ideas. This can be done by mixing ingredients from prior work.

Suppose there are two important papers in the literature. p_1 = {A, B, C, and D}, p_2 = {C, D, and E} where A, B, etc. are ideas.

{A, B, E} can be a new paper.

However, you must ask: Does the new combination make sense?

Another possibility is to make a new paper based on the following: {A, C, X} where X is something new.

Writing the Paper

Do not mention when a paper was first written and when it was revised. If the referee figures out that the paper was rejected more than once, he/she is more likely to recommend rejection. It is best to write the paper quickly. Once the ideas of a publishable paper are roughly formulated, writing should be done within a month. Otherwise, you might lose interest. About half of your writing time should be devoted to writing the main body of the paper, which should be done first. The remainder of your effort should be devoted to writing the introduction and conclusion.

Get Their Attention Early

Provide evidence why your paper is interesting in the introduction and abstract. Referees make up their minds in first 15 minutes. For this reason, your cover letter, title page, and abstract must be perfect. If the referees don't like a paper, they begin to look for reasons why the paper should be rejected. Also, if the referee loses interest from reading the introduction, he might postpone reading the paper. If a paper is set aside, it could be several months the referee picks up the paper again, probably if and when he/she receives a reminder. Do not repeat the concluding remarks in the introduction.

Short Introduction

If the introduction is more than 2 pages or 15% of the paper, it is too long.

If you write more than two pages, then

1. you are talking a lot about other people, in which case you are sending a signal that your contribution is minor relative to the literature, or
2. you are talking too much about technical details, which do not belong in the introduction.

Relevancy Test

Provide citations, statistics, or anecdotes of real world examples. Then the referee cannot say the paper is uninteresting, the most common reason for rejection. If the referee says your paper is not interesting, this is a value judgment and there is no appeal. Editors will not publish an "uninteresting" paper. One important purpose of the introduction is to prevent the referees from doing this.

Avoid the First Person

Some authors do get away with using the pronoun "I." Referees are generally biased against egocentric persons. "The paper achieves...." sounds better and more humble than "I did this." Also, avoid starting a paragraph with the word "I".

Respect your Colleagues

Emphasize the importance of your paper, but not at the expense of others. They will probably be your referees. When mentioning the works of others, avoid using negative terms.

"The deficiency of Smith's approach is..."
"The problems of these papers..."

Papers that attack others are likely to be rejected, especially if the one you criticize is asked to be a reviewer for your paper. If you offend the referee by your thoughtless comments, this paper and many of your future papers will have no place to go.

Select your Referees

Limitations

Do not apologize. Acknowledge the limitations of the approach only once. But you do not need to apologize for what the paper cannot do.

Interesting abstract

Write the abstract only after the conclusion is written. The referees read it more often than any other paragraph in the paper. In 15 seconds, you have to convince the referees (and readers) that they should continue with the rest of the paper. Give the paper an eye-catching title. If the title is boring, readers will skip your paper even when it is published and the paper will not generate many citations. Giving a title to a paper is like naming your child. The title should be short. One line is best, but try not to use more than two lines in any case.

Include references of your colleagues because this increases the chance that they will become referees. Include references to people with whom you have had favorable correspondence. This is not to bias opinions, but to get a fair hearing. Referees have to make a conscious effort and be alert in order to be fair to unknown authors.

References

An article is considered "important:" if it is cited 30 times or more by others. You can cite your own related papers, provided that they were published or are forthcoming in a prestigious journal. But do not cite too many.

Do not cite your own unpublished papers or publications in an obscure journal. The editor may conclude that your current paper should also be published in an obscure journal. Even with double blind reviews, one can often guess the identity of the author of a paper because of references and writing style, etc. If some referees consistently recommend rejection of your papers, do not include their papers in your references.

Choosing the Best Journal

It is best to choose your target journal early, when you first start writing the paper. Then you will prepare your paper with the journal's requirements in mind. This is more efficient than having to reformat the paper at a later stage.

A logical early step is to make a list of the journals that you and your colleagues read. This list is likely to contain journals in the field of your paper. You must ensure that the topic of your paper fits within the scope of the journal that you select.

At one extreme are the highly rated journals with large circulations, such as the Lancet or the New England Journal of Medicine, which accepts 10% or less of the many manuscripts that it receives. With some papers, you may wish to consider a new journal. New journals are usually actively looking for papers and you have a better chance for acceptance. However, many have very small circulations and new journals may not be indexed on Index Medicus or be listed in Current Contents. In addition, some of these journals fail. Although the audience may be small, if it is your target audience, this type of journal is worth considering.

Most papers will be sent to journals that are between these two extremes. The problem is that you can only submit your paper to one journal at a time. Then you must patiently wait for about 2-3 months for an answer. If you submit your paper to one top quality journal after another and your paper is not at that level, you will waste time. Meanwhile, another author may successfully publish a paper on exactly the same subject as yours in a respectable, but not top quality journal. If this happens, it reduces the value of your article. Therefore, it is important to know the quality of your article and to send it to a journal of corresponding quality.

It is very important to review the Instructions to Authors of your target journal. Editors change and update these instructions from time to time, so you should not assume that you know the instructions from past experience. There is usually a purpose statement, where the editors state what kind of articles they prefer to publish. Most journals now have their Instructions to Authors posted online.

Other factors to consider in the choice of a target journal include:

1. Who reads the journal? Are they the best audience for your paper?
2. How large is the circulation?
3. What is the time between acceptance and publication?
4. What is the Impact Factor of the journal? (How important is the journal?)

5. What is the acceptance rate? (Usually inversely related to importance and Impact Factor)
6. Do the major abstracting and indexing services cover the journal? (Index Medicus, Current Contents, etc.)

If you are unsure if your paper will be acceptable to a specific journal, you can write a letter to the editor giving the title and a brief summary and ask him if the paper fits within the scope of the journal. This is best done while the paper is in preparation in order to avoid losing time.

Choose your own referee?

Often, the editor will select your referees from the authors in your references. Whether your paper is accepted or not primarily depends on who referees it. Important references and references written by your preferred reviewers should be mentioned in the first page of your paper.

Below is a reference to a very interesting article on choosing your own referee. As many of you know, many medical and scientific journals allow authors submitting papers to suggest reviewers for their paper. In addition, authors may list reviewers whom they would prefer not review their papers. In the study, cited below, the authors examined the outcome of this approach and compared it with the outcome seen when authors did not request referees. This study was performed for only one journal, the British Journal of Surgery, but it showed that referees chosen by the editor were significantly more critical than those chosen by the authors.

This data suggests that authors submitting papers to journals, which allow this practice, should take advantage of it. Thus, if you know of someone working in the same field as you who is critical of your work, you should ask that he or she not be selected to review your paper. This means that you should also work to identify colleagues in the same field as you who are sympathetic to your work and request that they review your papers.

References

A comparison of reports from referees chosen by authors or journal editors in the peer review process. Earnshaw JJ, Farndon JR, Guillou PJ, Johnson CD, Murie JA, Murray GD. Ann R Coll Surg Engl 2000 Apr;82(4 Suppl):133-5.

Coates R, Sturgeon B, Bohannan J, Pasini E. Language and publication in "Cardiovascular Research" articles. Cardiovasc Res 2002 Feb 1;53(2):279-85. Coates R, et al.

Chapter 4. Writing for Medical Industry

Overview of Drug and Medical Device Development

In the United States, medical devices and pharmaceuticals must be approved by the Food and Drug Administration (FDA). This includes a wide variety of substances and devices. The approval of a new drug or device by the FDA is a complex, multi-step process and the medical writer needs to have a clear understanding of this overall process. This review will focus on the requirements in the USA for the sake of simplicity. There are more definitive reviews of this subject available (Parisian 2001) which the writer may need to consult for specifics. The requirements of the European Union are different, but there is a trend towards harmonization of all international drug regulations (Nightingale, 1995). However, each country has its own regulations.

In the United States, these regulations developed over the past century. The Federal Food, Drug and Cosmetic Act of 1938 and the 1962 Kefauver-Harris Amendments to this Act were important legislative steps taken to clarify and strengthen the role of the FDA in this process.

Sequence of drug development

Before being marketed and used in patient care, a new drug or medical device goes through a sequence of stages to define its pharmacology, safety and efficacy. In addition, tolerability and side effects are studied in detail. Under special circumstances, the sequence may be modified. For example, a drug for a serious disease without other remedies may undergo an accelerated development process. As drugs go through the development process, they may be eliminated for one reason or another. In fact, the goal of the drug companies is to eliminate unlikely candidates as early as possible in order to reduce the expenses of drug development.

The stages are:
1. Pharmacologic screening of new drug candidates
2. Testing in laboratory models or animals
3. Filing of an IND (Investigational New Drug) or IDE (Investigational Device Exemption) application
4. Clinical research in humans (phases I, II, and III)
5. Filing of NDA (New Drug Application) or PMA (Premarketing Approval Application)
6. Post marketing surveillance after approval (phase IV)

The time course for development of new drugs varies widely and depends on the type of drug being developed and the targeted disease. For example, development of antimicrobial agents can proceed quickly, with testing in animal models and humans. However, the development of drugs for cancer or for AIDS (Acquired Immune Deficiency Syndrome) is more difficult and requires more time for testing. Despite these factors, the overall time frame for development of a new drug is 7 to 12 years. Because of all the problems and pitfalls in drug development, only one in about every 10,000 candidates is finally approved as a new drug. The costs for drug development are large and continue to increase. In certain patient populations it may be more difficult to develop drugs, for example, the elderly.

A target disease may be identified by a pharmaceutical company and development of a drug for this disease started. This involves research into the anatomy, pharmacology, and pathophysiology of this disease. This then allows potential drug candidates to be designed and synthesized. Drug candidates must first pass a battery of pharmacological screening tests to identify the potential effects of the drug on the target disease. In addition, testing is carried out to examine drug safety. The group of drug candidates is then gradually reduced to identify a more select group with greater potential. This nonclinical research is conducted in strict adherence to FDA requirements to minimize the use of animals. However, at a certain stage, animals are used, because their metabolism mimics that of humans, and because this allows an estimation of the appropriate dose of each drug. Only the most likely drug candidates are allowed to proceed to human testing.

The Investigational New Drug (IND) Application

Once a likely drug candidate is identified, the sponsor (almost always a pharmaceutical company) requests FDA approval to begin clinical testing in human beings. The first step for this strictly regulated process is to file an IND (Investigational New Drug) application. The goal of this process is to minimize the risk to human beings during clinical trials. The IND application includes five important components.

1. All available information on the drug or device including its form of administration
2. Nonclinical data from animal studies that support the use of the drug

3. The Investigator's Brochure, which summarizes all of the above information
4. General plan of investigation for at least one year
5. Proposed protocol for the first human clinical trial

An FDA reviewer will be assigned to the application and will refer questions or deficiencies to the sponsor of the drug or device. The investigator can begin the proposed clinical trial within 30 days of the IND filing, unless he is informed otherwise by the FDA.

Clinical Trial Protocol

The clinical trial protocol is a key document, which is fundamental to the subsequent clinical trial report. The protocol provides the basis for the clinical trial, key references, objectives and methods, and usually will specify the method of analysis with the required endpoints. Protocol design is beyond the scope of this discussion. Major items included in all protocols include the following:

1. objectives, which must be clearly defined
2. inclusion and exclusion criteria
3. drug treatment or the regime or methods by which the medical device will be used or applied
4. endpoints, clinical or pharmacological
5. definition of failure and success
6. statistical design and analysis

A good protocol design enables the investigator to proceed in a systematic matter to determine the efficacy and safety of the drug or device. Importantly, a good protocol design also safeguards the safety of human subjects.

Study Phases in Clinical Research

Clinical research in a new drug and humans proceeds through several phases. One phase must be completed before the next one begins. The most important are phases I, II, and III. Data from studies in these phases will be used to determine whether the drug will be approved for marketing or not.

Phase I studies include those of pharmacological activity, pharmacokinetics, and basic tolerance. These are short-term studies with a single dose lasting about two weeks. The size of the studies is limited to less than 10 subjects per trial. The population consists of healthy volunteers without the target disease.

Phase II studies include those of effective dose regimen and early efficacy and safety status. The studies are also short-term, lasting about two months or less, and include 50 to 300 subjects depending on trial design. Patients with the target disease are included, but are carefully selected.

Phase III studies examine the efficacy for the main indication, rates of adverse events, and the optimal dosage. In general, these are longer-term studies. The number of subjects will range from the hundreds to the thousands, depending on the target disease. Patients with the target disease are included. Phase III studies are major clinical research studies and this the final phase of study in which the bulk of information on humans is gathered to support government approval of the drug or device.

If the studies resulting from these first three phases are favorable, the sponsor will request formal approval from the FDA to market the drug or device. This will require preparation and submission of an NDA, PMA or 510k application.

New Drug Application

The NDA, or new drug application, includes all nonclinical, clinical and other data about the drug or device. The purpose of this application is to request FDA approval for marketing of the drug for a given therapeutic indication to a defined target population. The corresponding document in Canada is the NDS or New Drug Submission, and in Europe it is the MAA or Marketing Approval Authorization.

The contents of these documents are relatively similar and it is expected that in the future there will be increasing harmonization. This trend towards consistency and harmonization is favorable for the pharmaceutical companies, who seek greater efficiency in drug development. It is also favorable for the medical writers, who must prepare these documents.

The NDA includes all information on the drug. The data is presented in special formats to facilitate review by the FDA. The FDA reviewer reviews the appropriateness of this information, but may work with other experts within the FDA. For example, to review the statistical analysis and numerical data, he may request a statistical expert in the FDA to review that part of the application. The overall decision on approval will depend on the relationship of potential risks to the benefits of the drug. This in turn depends on the nature of the disease in question. For major diseases with high mortality, such as cancer, a higher-level of side effects is acceptable. However, a high level of side effects is not acceptable for a new drug for the treatment of a relatively benign condition, such as hypertension. These decisions are based upon scientific analysis and concern for the patient.

Phase IV of Clinical Research

If the drug or device is approved by the FDA, it can be marketed with the United States. During this time, the medical writer will be involved in communicating the information on the drug to a wider audience, including physicians, other medical professionals, and the lay public. Study of the drug continues in phase IV. Phase IV includes a variety of trials that seek to expand the understanding of the new drug, its efficacy, and side effects. Trials may be conducted to examine this drug in expanded or new patient populations. This might include studies of the drug in patients with renal insufficiency, for example. While the studies must be scientifically valid, they are less rigorous than a studies conducted in the earlier phases. Trials started after an NDA has been filed but before approval is received are termed IIIb. If the drug or device sponsor wishes to examine the use of the drug in a completely different patient population, it may be necessary to return to phase I, II, and III studies. In addition, the drug sponsor is required to monitor the drug for safety and adverse effects as the drug is used more widely and in larger patient populations. Rare side effects, in fact, will not be detected before drug approval, simply due to the number of patients studied. This ongoing postmarketing surveillance serves the goal of maximal safety for the patient while providing ongoing therapeutic benefits.

Types of Documents for Medical Industry

There is a wide range of medical documents used in the development of a new drug or medical device. However, all of these documents fall into two broad categories: first, regulatory documents that focus on the requirements for government approval; and second, documents aimed at the broader medical community. One useful way to approach the creation of these documents is to first consider the audience. This includes their needs, their perceptions, and their preconceived ideas. This allows the medical writer to create a document that is most useful to the target audience. Keeping the audience in mind during the creation of each document allows the writer to be more efficient in transmitting information.

Regulatory Documents

Most writing in the pharmaceutical industry focuses on regulatory documents that are part of the drug approval process. These documents describe the results of clinical trials, and tend to be very technical in nature. Quite often the documents contain tables and graphics that are derived from the clinical trial. The most common of these documents are research reports for individual drug trials, overview documents which review results from several trials, and supportive material for the above.

Foundation reports of research studies detail the results of each specific trial. This may include investigations into a drug's actions, safety, or efficacy. Each phase of drug development and research may involve a series of individual trials, each of which requires an individual report. For each trial, the objectives, methods, results, and conclusions, and supplemental information, must be documented. The format for these reports depends on regulatory guidelines, the research discipline, and corporate rules.

Summary and overview documents collect information from several trials into an overview of a specific aspect of drug or medical device action. For example, in order to understand the overall efficacy of a given form of therapy, it is necessary to review all of the studies of its efficacy. The same principle is true when results of drug safety are reviewed, for example. In the creation of such documents, it may be necessary to explain why some results are in apparent or real conflict. The interpretation of such conflicting data may be critical in determining the ultimate therapeutic profile of the new drug or medical device.

Supportive materials for drug or medical device submissions provide additional information and may be required by regulatory guidelines. A drug submission may require documents that summarize the drug's development strategy, review key decisions made in meetings with regulatory agencies, and sometimes listings of all participating investigators. The Investigator's Brochure is a specialized supportive document that details information collected at various stages throughout the development of a new drug or medical device. Of course, the creation of a listing, appendix, bibliography, or similar document is not interesting for the medical writer, but nonetheless an important part of a regulatory submission.

Documents on Medical Devices or Drugs for the Medical Community

Regulatory documents are generally considered confidential

and the targeted audience requires more information than a practicing clinician or pharmacist. Another group of documents is designed to communicate in a more abbreviated fashion aspects of a new drug or device to a clinical audience, including nurses, physicians and pharmacists. These documents are not so formal and contain less information than regulatory documents. There are a wide variety of communication forms used to reach the general medical audience. This includes manuscripts for scientific journals, abstracts, slides, posters, and advertising copy. Materials for professional meetings may include several of these. For example, an abstract for presentation at a scientific meeting may allow only one page or even one paragraph to summarize a complete clinical study. Or a presentation at a scientific meeting may be limited to 10 minutes to cover the same amount of material. In this case, the writer must design a document to include and emphasize the most important points for the target audience.

Medical communication or writing is often are used to persuade the clinician of the value of a new drug or product. Whether or not the readers are persuaded is dependent on the mode and style of the presentation. The communication must include the key messages, must be limited in size, and must be persuasive but balanced. If a paper is clearly one-sided and over emphasizes one aspect of the results, it will not appear to be balanced and will not be credible. Regulatory documents benefit from having a captive audience. However, journal articles and other types of writing must compete with other articles for the reader's attention. If the articles are not interesting or if they do not engage the reader's attention early, the reader will move on to something else. Techniques to catch the reader's attention include using titles with unique words and presenting key data early in the text. With experience, medical writers can learn ways to capture the reader's attention.

Professional Roles of the Medical Writer

Effective medical writing involves a variety of skills. In the medical device and pharmaceutical industries, medical writing is done by teams of writers. The goal is to prepare high quality documents to support the new drug for the commercial success of the product but also to contribute to improved health care. Medical writing groups must include a wide range of talents to serve all of these functions. Medical writers within a group may individually specialize in various aspects of document preparation. Sometimes regulatory and medical communication groups will be in separate departments, for example, research and marketing. There may be other corporate departments that provide additional support services to the medical writing group, such as a informational technology and the like. Important support functions for the writing group include technical editing, quality control, electronic publishing, document management, and administrative support. In additional to these functions, secretarial support, proofreading, and professional training are also important.

Medical writers usually have an educational background in science as well as language arts. Approximately half have a graduate or professional degree. Detailed information on medical writers has been collected by the American Medical Writers Association by Losi in 1987. Individuals interested in medical writing can obtain additional training in communication by taking college courses or continuing education programs. The AMWA offers such programs. For medical writers currently at a university, they can consider combining degrees in two separate areas, for example, a major and minor in a scientific field and in a communication field. Writers with more scientific background may be better suited for regulatory writing, whereas writers with more language background may be better at writing publication, although this may be variable in individual cases.

Medical writers must be able to work alone, but in today's competitive environment, they often work as part of a team. Within a pharmaceutical organization or medical device company, such a team may include medical writers, a programmer, a biostatistician, a clinical trial specialist, and a physician. The roles of these various individuals will change through the product lifecycle, but the medical writer will have an important role during document production. Thus, the medical writer must balance his time between actual writing and meeting with other team members. In addition, good listening skills may be as important as good writing skills. The collaboration between the medical writer and the other team members can be enhanced by the effective use of the most modern publishing and information technology. Amazing advances have been made in recent years in publishing information technology. The medical writer must keep up with these advances, and in fact, is dependent on them.

Publishing and Information Technology

Ongoing developments in this field require the ongoing attention of the medical writer. The practice of medical writing in pharmaceutical or medical device research is strongly affected by developments in this field. Regulatory documents can be very large in terms of weight and bulk. Medical companies seek to be competitive and to reduce time but not quality in the production of these documents. The overall production of a new drug is very expensive and this expense can be reduced dramatically by saving time. Information technology assists these companies, and allows processing, storing and retrieving of these complex documents. Optical imaging of paper documents allows companies to manage their proprietary information in a secure and efficient fashion. Electronic publishing systems use filters to convert documents from various sources into one coherent structure. The sources may include text, spreadsheet or statistical data, computer graphics and optical images. In this setting the medical writer is forced to rely on the technological staff who run the electronic publishing infrastructure. The complexity of these systems also introduces various problems. For example, one problem may be the interface between two different types of software using different document formats. The capabilities of the software in the future may include such things as compliance management and the ability to assemble, collaborate distribute, review, and publish regulatory documents. The publishing capabilities may also include forms-based documents, and enhanced functionality for the creation and maintenance of tables of content and cross-references.

New drug applications consist of large amounts of drug data with detailed reports of the drug's properties, development, and testing results. The FDA requires that its reviewers have access to the primary information on which the NDA is based. A typical NDA consists of tens of thousands of pages of text, grafts, charts, case reports, and clinical notes. It includes a complete history of the drug from the time of its initial discovery and includes early studies in animals, as well as clinical trials. It also includes details of the manufacturing process and how the drug will be packaged, labeled, and marketed to the public and medical profession. All of this means that paper and the NDA do not arrive at the FDA by mail in envelopes but instead by truck in boxes. However, recently NDA's have been arriving at the FDA in computer-readable format.

For obvious reasons the FDA and companies are trying to select a common standard as the foundation of the electronic publishing system. The FDA is now requiring medical companies to use information technology to speed the approval process. The New Drug Application, or NDA, is no longer simply a paper application, but must be in the form of the Computer Assisted New Drug Application or CANDA.

Computer-readable submissions for drugs, vaccines, and medical devices shorten review time, and eliminate the need to search through large stacks of paper documents. If the medical reviewer has a specific question about a patient or other aspect of the record, under the old system, he would have to send a request to the document room and this could take a day to obtain. With a computer-readable format, the same search can be done in a matter of minutes. Computer-readable submissions are approved about six months faster than traditional paper submissions.

It is also worth noting that the current practice during clinical trials is for physicians to record the data on a computer, which is then transmitted electronically to the drug sponsor's computers. This method is obviously faster, and it also markedly reduces errors in data recording. The computer can be used to check the data for errors at the time of submission.

This is a rapidly evolving field, and what is written here will be out of date by the time it is published. Current electronic publishing systems promote the sharing and reviewing of information internally. They also allow pharmaceutical and medical device companies to reuse and repackage their information for other regulatory submissions. Proper leveraging of technology by pharmaceutical companies can allow them to reduce their costs dramatically. A modern electronic publishing system allows information to be gathered from various sources (for example, from over 100 different file formats). It allows a dynamic document to be created, complete with a table of contents and hyperlinks to cross-referenced information that are automatically updated. This software allows publication of this dynamic document with control of page layout and the ultimate format. Such a system also can markedly reduce the difficulty of reviewing, revising and the publishing the document. In addition, by collating all information into one dynamic document, the company allows the entire team responsible for the submission to review it and make appropriate changes. As stated above, electronic submissions bring faster review, which translates into savings for the sponsoring company. The end result is high quality and accurate drug submissions, which are on time. The product development lifecycle can be accelerated and the information assets of the company can be more efficiently used. New drug submission formats will no doubt emerge in the future. Such systems can also reduce the risk of compliance problems and allow the company to manage this risk. Process bottlenecks can be identified and corrected. For all of these pressing reasons, is expected that development in this field will continue to progress. The medical writer, especially if he is a member of the team in one of these companies, must keep up with the rapid developments in this field. This represents a challenge and an opportunity for professional growth.

Regulatory Submissions Structure

A decade of work on a drug or a device to may go into a regulatory submission. Many technical specialists provide input, including bench scientists, clinical physicians, statisticians and medical writers. FDA standards require that the submission be submitted in volumes, in proper order. When we consider the entire drug submission, it resembles a well-designed building with a foundation, support columns, and a roof. The submission must have balance in order to be believable, the same way a building must be built on level ground. The foundation of the submission consists of a large body of research reports and studies. In addition, other supporting documents make up the foundation. The support columns of the building include the integrated summaries. Finally, the roof and the dome of the building are made up of the comprehensive summary and the proposed labeling for the drug or device. The product labeling may be thought of as the distilled summary of the new therapy. However, the overall strength of the submission is only as strong as its foundation, which is based on the individual research reports. These reports must still be written by someone with medical writing skills. The NDA submission has 13 required chapters or sections. The sections can be sent for individual review by specialists within the FDA. These chapters are listed on the table below.

Table. Structure of an New Drug Application (NDA)

1. Table of contents
2. Comprehensive summary
3. Chemistry, manufacturing, and controls system
4. Samples, methods validation, and labeling package
5. Nonclinical pharmacology and toxicology section
6. Human pharmacokinetics and bioavailability section
7. Microbiology section (for antibiotics).
8. Clinical data section
9. Safety update report
10. Statistical section
11. Case report tabulations
12. Case report forms
13. Patent information

Reports of Research Trials

The reports of research trials conducted during drug development form the foundation of a regulatory submission. Each trial requires a formal report, which completely documents the methods, results, and their interpretation. Clinical trial reports have a basic structure and require a certain strategy to write.

Because they represent formal documentation of a drug or device trial, there are specific guidelines governing their content, format, and medium. These guidelines vary depending on the type of research trial, for example, nonclinical versus clinical, and with the therapeutic category of the drug. Of course, the efficient development of new drugs and the publication of research requires that the formats for these reports be standardized across different countries. The European Community has been active in standardizing requirements for drug research reports so that one standard could apply to all countries. The ongoing work of the International Conference on Harmonization (Nightingale 1995) is an important part of this. These regulations remain subject to interpretation, but this trend towards harmonization is favorable.

Research reports have a structure consisting of introduction, methods, results, and conclusions. There are differences in these reports between clinical and nonclinical reports. For example, nonclinical trials in animals would tend to contain certain subsections not found in clinical trials in humans. The research reports lay the foundation for a more comprehensive review of all available information on a new drug or device. Without extensive documentation of a new drug by a collection of research trials, an overview and high-level comparison cannot be made. The collection of research reports is fundamental to the overall regulatory submission. In the United States, the FDA has specific guidelines regarding the reporting of clinical trials. The medical writer must always verify the report structure required by checking the latest guidelines of the regulatory bodies before creating his report.

Strategy for writing a research report

When writing a research report, it is important to communicate the purpose, methods, and findings of the trial in sufficient detail so that others can independently evaluate the outcome of the trial. The research report must be factual, scientific, and detailed. It must be written in a direct and straightforward manner. Certain strategies can be used to do this. For example, the sentence structure must be kept simple. The writer must provide navigational clues to the reader, such as a table of contents, section titles, and section numbers. Data are condensed into tables to support the statements in the text. Trends from the data can be shown on graphs. Cross-references to other such sections should be included. Appendices with supporting data can be added at the end.

There are other differences between a research report and journal manuscript. The research report targets the reviewers of a regulatory agency, while a journal manuscript must capture the interest of the larger medical community. The research report provides comprehensive results, but a journal manuscript will only include the major and most interesting results. A research report minimizes the use of the medical literature but a journal article will compare the results to the medical literature. A research report may be thousands of pages long but a journal article will be limited to 5 – 14 pages. A research report will use a table of contents for easy navigation but a journal manuscript will use only section headings. The larger size of a research report requires these navigational aids. The journal's editorial style will dictate the journal report format. Logically, the research reports must be written before the overall review documents or the regulatory submission. However, since there is strong pressure to bring drugs to market rapidly and efficiently, the time frames for writing these reports may overlap. The use of electronic publishing systems may be used to facilitate this.

Summary and Review Reports

Summary documents combine the complex facts regarding a

new drug or device into an understandable message. Some may focus on specific aspects, such as toxicology, clinical safety, or clinical efficacy. The creation of such documents requires focus on the overall goal. Of course, the writer will first focus on specific agency guidelines for a particular document. Also a writer must understand the relationships of the summary document to all other documents regarding the new drug or device. This allows the proper perspective to be maintained. Also, the document's message must come from an unbiased presentation of existing evidence. Scientists and clinicians directly working on a new drug may unintentionally become biased. The potential for adverse events or side effects must be very carefully examined. The successful creation of the document for a regulatory body assumes that the writer understands the guidelines from the regulatory agency and is also able to use them on a practical level. The writer may take a checklist approach to make sure all requirements are fulfilled, but a must also be able to interpret the requirements within the context of the unique properties of the new drug or device. The understanding of the complex interrelationships between the overview document and other documents regarding the new drug is very important. The writer attempts to build one piece of evidence on top of another to support the overall conclusion. Each conclusion must be logically presented and include the findings that support it. A regulatory submission will consist of a series of defined sections reporting on each aspect of the new drug or device.

Support Materials for Submissions

Supportive material complements the regulatory submission. This material may include short pieces of text, tables that continue over many pages, or documents such as the Investigator's Brochure. In a New Drug Application, Section 2 is titled "Comprehensive Summary". This area provides basic information for all the regulatory reviewers. Section 2B, Pharmacological Class, Scientific Rationale and Potential Clinical Benefits, includes several important points. It includes a definition of the pharmacological class of the drug under study, the scientific rationale of the research program, and a precise description of the clinical benefits expected from the drug. This section must be concise and summarizes the science behind the drug itself. In contrast, section 8B, Background Overview of Clinical Investigations, is primarily directed towards clinical reviewers. This text documents includes the following points: rationale for the key design features of the clinical trials (such as dosing, controls, and endpoints), relationship of clinical pharmacology to trial design, regulatory guidelines followed, key decisions between sponsor and agency, demographic subgroups chosen, safety and efficacy issues, and areas for further research. These short narrative documents can be prepared before studies are completed and updated as work progresses on the drug. In addition, it is important to lay out the rationale for scientific work before the work is started to ensure its quality.

Another part of the document that can be prepared at the beginning of the work, are the tabular summaries. Sometimes the formats for these are specified by the FDA or another regulatory body. The format of the table can be created at the beginning of the study and data filled in as it is collected. Early agreement on the format of the table can improve efficiency by avoiding late stage disagreements. In addition it is important to provide consistency for all the tables in an NDA for ease in reading. Their summaries will be part of several different sections of an NDA.

The sections on clinical pharmacology trials, controlled clinical tiles, uncontrolled clinical trials, and other trials and information may all require tabular summaries. Electronic publishing systems support clear table designs and it is expected that future software will provide further advances in this area.

Investigator's Brochure

The investigator's brochure (IB) is a compilation of nonclinical and clinical data about the new drug. It allows enrollments of patients or subjects into a study in an informed manner. The IB is updated periodically as new data and trial results are collected on the drug. It can be regarded as an overview or summary document, but as its primary purpose is to enable the investigator to conduct an ethical clinical trial, it can be considered as a supportive document. The earliest version of the IB may only include nonclinical information. This is at the stage when human trials are just beginning. Then as clinical trial results are accumulated, the IB will be expanded. The IB includes several specified sections and these may be updated or changed by the regulatory bodies. At this time the required sections include the title page; table of contents; summary; introduction; physical, chemical, and pharmaceutical properties; nonclinical pharmacology; toxicology; nonclinical pharmacokinetics and drug metabolism; clinical pharmacology and pharmacokinetics; clinical trials; product information; and bibliography.

Electronic Publishing Systems

As noted, there is increasing pressure on pharmaceutical companies to produce new drug submissions in a rapid timeframe and with high quality. This places the medical writer under great pressure. Different sections of drugs submissions are often referred as "dossiers" especially among the European agencies. Electronic publishing systems allow more rapid production of these different sections and also allow for efficient reuse and repackaging of textual and tabular information. The use of an electronic publishing system to produce such a document or regulatory submission relies on the medical writer, who is a communications expert charged with coordinating and packaging data from a variety of technical experts, which may include statisticians and clinicians, among others. It is fortunate that we now have this advanced technology to help manage the current information explosion in medicine and other sciences. Electronic publishing systems also allow version control of the document. However any tool is only good as its user and is this principal clearly applies to the medical writer and the electronic publishing system. The burden is on the medical writer to stay updated in this rapidly evolving field.

Writing Strategy

It is important to have a clear strategy when creating any document. Regulatory submissions require the presentation of huge amounts of information from research programs that may be complex and have many facets. Here the audience is captive in the sense that the regulatory reviewers are required to read the document. However, documents for publication must compete

journal editors require that articles be reviewed by a select group of peers in the scientific community. Of course the editors also carefully review the paper. The peer review process itself can be subject to ethical problems and constraints. The peer review can also increase the time and cost of publication. However, it has withstood the test of time as a valuable screening process for scientific manuscripts and no superior system has emerged.

Promotional Material for Marketing

Drugs occupy an important position within the spectrum of healthcare products. They are subject to strict regulatory controls. Of course, they have a certain economic value and must be sold by the companies to generate revenues to offset the costs of development and production. In particular, a new drug requires promotion and marketing so that the medical community can learn about it and its potential benefits. Marketing materials for drugs are subject to ethical as well as regulatory controls. Promotion of a new drug may be considered within the marketing mix, which can be viewed from the standpoint of the 4 P's.

1. Product: the actual drug and its benefits
2. Place: distribution channels from the company to pharmacies to the patient
3. Price: cost not only at the retail level, but also including all costs to bring the product to market.
4. Promotion: communication of the first three points to the patient and the physician

A fifth P that is sometimes added is Position.

5. Position: differentiation of this product from potential competitors.

Position is more important when there are many competing drugs for a given disease or condition. Drugs can be differentiated from competitors in terms of side effect profile, class action, or potential benefits for specific demographic groups.

Consideration of these factors allows the company to create a marketing plan, which will require marketing materials to communicate aspects of the drug or medical device to the healthcare practitioners and to the public.

Promotional materials can be divided into several categories, for example, advertising material, personal selling support material, sales promotion material, and publicity material. Advertising material will consist of text and graphics for publication in journals. Personal selling material will be material that the sales representative can use during visits to physicians. This might include copies of journal articles or reference texts. Sales promotion material might include training materials or handouts such as a guide to the new drug. Publicity material will include lay press advertising, congress materials and press releases.

In creating materials it is important to recall that drugs in the United States can only be promoted for approved indications. It is important to keep an overview of the entire drug development process when creating materials.

References

Medical Writing in Drug Development: A Practical Guide for Pharmaceutical Research by Robert J. Bonk, Haworth Press; 1st edition (January 15, 1998) ISBN: 0789004496

Parisian S, FDA: Inside and Out. Fast Horse Press, Front Royal, VA. 2001.

Nightingale SL, Challenges in International Harmonization, Drug Information Journal 29: 1-9, 1995.

Friedman LM, Furberg CD, and DeMets DL. Fundamental of Clinical Trials. Springer International Publishng, Switzerland, 2015.

Chapter 5. Special Types of Writing

Curriculum Vitae and Resumes

Curriculum Vitae

Of course, it is important for a medical writer to know how to write a curriculum vitae. You may need to do this for yourself, if you need to apply for a position, or you may need to help a client with his curriculum vitae. A document similar to the curriculum vitae is the resume. This is a shorter summary of experience and skills of an individual that is sometimes used in job applications. The resume has a different format than the curriculum vitae and is not as inclusive. When applying for a position in Europe, the Middle East, Africa, or Asia you should expect to submit a curriculum vitae, rather than a resume. The resume is used more commonly in North America. When applying for an academic, educational, scientific or research position, a curriculum vitae should be used. Curriculum vitae are also used when applying for grants or fellowships.

A curriculum vitae is longer than a resume and is a more detailed summary of your skills and background. It will include a summary of your educational and academic background, and it as well as teaching and research experience, publications, awards, honors, presentations, affiliations and many other details. It may also include courses you have taught, licenses, and your diplomas. You may need to have different versions of your curriculum vitae for use for different purposes. For example, you would use a different version of your curriculum vitae in applying for clinical positions than for applying for academic or research positions. You start by making a list of your background information, and then organize it into appropriate categories. This list will normally include dates for all of your activities. It is useful to review sample CVs from other individuals. This can also be done on the Internet by reviewing CVs from individuals and fields similar to your own.

When applying for a position, the first impression is the one that matters the most, so your CV needs to be perfect. This means that you must choose an appropriate curriculum vitae format. As stated above, you should have targeted and focused versions of your curriculum vitae and use them at the appropriate times. Normally your CV will not include your photo, your salary history, reasons for leaving prior positions, or references. References can be provided separately and are usually given upon request. It is important to double-check your CV for any typographical or grammatical errors. It is also useful to ask someone else to review it for you. This makes it easier to catch any mistakes. The CV should use formal and well-written language without slang. Needless to say, your CV should only include the truth. Many employers conduct reference and background checks and false claims or statements may be found out.

Your curriculum vitae should follow the five C's.
Clear - well organized and logical
Concise - relevant and necessary
Complete - includes everything needed.
Consistent – don't change styles or fonts
Current – up-to-date

Resumes

The object of a resume is to list your relevant skills and experience for an employment application. Resumes should be custom written for each job and employer. This means you must carefully read the requirements of the position in which you are interested and then write your resume to list these points in the same order.

Your resume should have correct spelling, appropriate grammar, and no typing mistakes. The format and feel of your resume should be good. Employers may receive many resumes for a given position and have a tendency to sort them early on based upon their appearance. Every mistake makes a manager question your care and attention to detail.

You must include good contact information. There is absolutely no reason to make it difficult for the employer to contact you. Give the potential employer your cell phone number even if you have to buy a mobile phone in order to find a position.

Your resume should include a section called Career Highlights and Qualifications. This section is a series of bullet points that emphasize your most important career experiences, skills, character traits, and key accomplishments from your work history. These should relate to the job to which you are applying.

For each former employer, clearly indicate the company name, your position and the dates of employment. You should provide a brief statement that tells what the company does, its products, sales and customers. Say exactly what you did for the company. For each prior employer, you should include a list of key contributions or key achievements.

Your educational background must be clear. This means dates of attendance and degrees must be given. Include a section that lists awards and other recognition. This can include extracurricular activities, or even philanthropic activities.

Cover letters

Whenever you send your curriculum vitae or resume to a potential employer, you must include a cover letter. There are generally three types of cover letters: the application letter, the prospecting letter, and the networking letter. The application letter is written in response to a known job opening. The prospecting letter inquires about possible positions in a given company. In a networking letter, you request information and assistance in your job search.

Your cover letter must be individualized for each job application. This means it must have the name of the person to whom you are writing. Do not send the same form letter to multiple employers. This would almost guarantee that your application would be thrown into the wastebasket. It is certainly easier and tempting to write a generic or blanket cover letter rather than putting in the extra work to individualize it. However, some employers receive hundreds of resumes for a given position. Your cover letter should emphasize your skills and experiences that are most relevant to the position that you are applying for. You should research the company before you write this letter and make sure that you understand the position that you are applying for.

Material for Scientific Meetings and Conferences

Medical conferences serve a valuable role because they allow rapid publication of new scientific information. Professional meetings require creation of several document types. These include abstracts submitted for consideration for presentation, slides and posters for actual presentations, and the proceedings of the entire conference. The rules for abstract presentation vary from conference to conference and are governed by the medical society involved. There are general medical conferences and also conferences for medical specialists. Sometimes prominent scientists and clinicians are invited to give presentations, but more commonly the clinician must submit a paper for consideration by the professional society. The submissions must meet strict criteria regarding format and are usually limited to one page. When writing an abstract the goals are first, acceptance and secondly, to create interest for the conference participants to attend the poster or slide session and thirdly, to document the research results. In general, abstracts follow the IMRAD format. The format requirements can be strict and if the writer does not follow them his paper may be rejected before it is even read. The format rules allow compilation of the abstracts into a meeting book without additional typesetting.

Writing Abstracts for Scientific Meetings

Writing an abstract for a scientific meeting that is effective can be a challenging task. Many scientific meetings are very competitive and making sure that your abstract is accepted over a competitor's can be difficult. It is best to start some time before the deadline, even if your data is not complete. This allows extra time for formatting and revisions. The abstract can oftentimes be written in rough form without the final data. This gives the author valuable information as to how much information will fit into the space allowed. It is important to read the abstract instructions and rules carefully. In addition, many abstract submission forms include a sample abstract, which also should be carefully examined. You may wish to assign responsibility for the actual formatting and printing of the abstract to a secretary, but the author must ensure that the format and rules are followed.

Format:

The abstract consists of the introduction, methods, results, and conclusions sections, although they may not be labeled as such depending on the format used. The introduction explains the purpose of the study and may describe the study design. Normally, references are not included as part of an abstract. Although you may refer to prior work in the introduction, you should not mention other authors' names. The methods section explains the methods used. Abbreviations should be chosen with care and, in most cases, are defined in the text. For example,

We studied pts with intraventricular conduction defects (IVCD)."

In a medical abstract, patients (i.e. "pts") may normally be abbreviated without defining it, but other abbreviations (i.e. IVCD) require definitions. The use of abbreviations is an area where you must check the rules carefully. When possible, it is good to include a figure or a table in the results section. However, tables must be carefully formatted so that they are clearly legible. Both tables and figures require clear labeling and should only use abbreviations already defined in the text. Correct formatting and placement of figures and tables requires good knowledge of the software being used and may require extra time. This is another reason to start your abstract early and not try to do at the last minute. A clear, well-labeled figure can make your abstract stand out from the competitors and adds greatly to the readability of your abstract. "A picture is worth a thousand words." It is worth the extra effort to do properly.

Conclusions of the abstract:

The conclusions should be relevant to the data and may include a direction for future research. In a medical abstract, the conclusions should be written to indicate their clinical relevance. Ask yourself the following question, "How does this scientific work benefit mankind?" Make sure that any potential benefit of your work is indicated in the conclusions.

If your software allows it, use the spell checker to check the spelling of all words. Often, medical or scientific terminology will not be included in the spell checker and must be checked independently. However, it is surprising how often this step will detect simple, but overlooked errors. All of the coauthors should be asked to read the abstract and give their suggestions. Make sure that their names are spelled correctly. If you misspell a coauthor's name, you may make an enemy. Also, ask several of your colleagues to read the abstract. They will give you valuable suggestions and feedback. Some abstract forms will also require you to select a category and keywords. This should be done by the author and not delegated to a secretary.

After you have submitted your abstract, meet with your

coauthors and plan how the work will continue. Even if the abstract is rejected, continued work or a look at the problem from a different angle may produce positive results. Sometimes, all that is required is a higher sample size. Make sure that the next time you submit an abstract, that it is better that the last time. You should look upon the whole process of abstract submission as a way for you to improve your abilities as a researcher and writer.

After papers are accepted normally they must be presented as either a slide presentation or a poster. The medical writer may be called upon to prepare presentations and either of these formats. Slide presentations are given to a larger audience but posters allow for direct individual interaction.

Scientific Posters

A scientific poster is a large document that is designed to communicate your research at a scientific meeting. It is composed of a short title, an introduction, an overview of your experimental methods, your results, some discussion of the results, references, and acknowledgment of financial support. Posters require careful design, and must follow a logical order. The formatting rules will vary from conference to conference. Format and size constraints must be examined before creation of the poster. Posters should combine diagrams and pictures with text to convey the overall message. The poster must be designed to be pleasing to the eye. In addition it can be very helpful to have handouts to give to those who visit the poster. When properly prepared someone normally can read your poster in less than 10 minutes.

Scientific posters offer some advantages over short talks at a scientific meeting. Presenting a poster allows you to interact personally with people who are interested in your research. You have the chance to meet people working in your field and to make friends and contacts. In addition a scientific poster is desirable when someone is not skillful at giving scientific talks. Also once a good scientific poster has been produced it can be presented at multiple meetings.

Scientific posters are presented in large rooms in which the participants are invited to walk around in and browse the posters. Of course people take advantage of this opportunity to socialize and there may be refreshments nearby. This can make the overall atmosphere somewhat less formal. You should assume that your poster will be placed between two posters that are very interesting and that you must make your poster equally interesting and entertaining.

A good approach is to make a rough draft first. This should be done at least one month before the due date. Then you need to invite several friends or colleagues to review your poster and give you feedback. The goal is to make sure that your poster is clear, easy to read, and interesting. Your colleagues can make suggestions on small sticky notes that you provide and they should comment on word count, flow of ideas, figure clarity, font size, spelling, etc.

Posters can be produced in several different ways. You can build a poster by pasting content on to A4 or 8.5 x 11 inch panels, which are then attached to the poster board at the meeting using pins. A second approach is to use layout software to design a poster, which is then printed on a large poster printer. This requires the use of a page layout application, which allows for text wrapping, text flow among associated text blocks, and other features. Your poster should include a good amount of whitespace, which makes the poster easier to read. Your poster should be designed so that it can be read from about 2 m (6 feet) distance. Try to limit the amount of text because this will maximize the chance that people will actually read your poster. Try to make your poster with 1000 words or less.

Your title should convey the main issue or question that your paper addresses. Some scientific meetings require that your abstract be included as part of your poster. You will have to follow the rules of the scientific meeting that you are attending. In your introduction, you try to get the viewer interested in the issue or question of your paper. In order to do this you should quickly place the issue in context. This section should be as short as possible while maintaining clarity. The background information given should be the minimum required. Graphs and figures should be clear and easy to understand. The conclusions, given at the end, should be succinct and clear.

Preparing Scientific Slide Presentations

Excellent scientific presentations can be given if adequate preparation is made. This preparation includes preparing slides and rehearsing the talk. The first thing to consider is the purpose of your presentation. You must also know who your audience is and what your goals are. You should start thinking about your presentations several weeks ahead of time. You need to know how much time you have available and what facilities are available in the meeting room. It's also useful to know who else will be speaking in the same session.

Typically there will be rules about the duration of a slide presentation that must be followed. Each slide should present one idea clearly and they should complement the oral presentation. A common mistake is to try to put too much textual information on a slide, which can make it difficult to read. No more than seven lines of text should be placed on a single slide. Slides must also include some whitespace. It is a mistake to try to force too much data into a slide or too many slides into a short presentation.

Slides have to be made carefully and you should make backup copies of your slides. The slides should be checked for spelling or grammatical errors. Visual aids include slides, video, overhead projector, computer presentation, and a whiteboard. It is very common today to use PowerPoint slides for presentations. Good slides serve two purposes: they amplify and clarify the message, and they help the speaker to keep on track.

In preparing a slide presentation, a master slide is first prepared. This slide is used as a template for other slides. The title should be greater than or equal to 32 points in size. It is important that your slides be legible from the back of the room. The most common error is to try to put too much information on a single slide. In order to avoid this slides should only include six to seven lines of text. You should show only one figure per slide. You should usually avoid using gimmicks such as animation. This should only be used when it strengthens your message.

It is important to rehearse your presentation beforehand. This can be done with colleagues or with your supervisor. It is also possible to make an audio or video tape recording of your speech and review the talk for errors in your speech. When speaking it is important for you to talk directly to your audience and to make eye contact with them. You should speak to your audience and not simply read your talk. You should not speak too close the microphone. But you should also use your pointer to highlight useful information on your slides. On average you should show one slide per minute.

When traveling to the meeting, carry your slides or computer in your hand luggage. You do not want to arrive at the conference with no presentation. Also you should bring your own pointer. You can prepare notes for your presentation but do not be dependent on them. Your slides can serve as your notes because they could prompt you during your speech. It is useful to arrive in the room early and to go to the podium and see how the equipment is laid out. You should familiarize yourself with the controls for the microphone, the slides, and the lights in the room. Occasionally one encounters a meeting room in which it is not possible for you to see your own slides on the screen during your speech. This makes it very difficult to give a presentation because you cannot use your slides to prompt yourself and because it is difficult to coordinate your speech with your slides. It is important to know about these problems ahead of time and not find out at the last minute. You also may wish to a glass of water available for your speech. In handling the question and answers after your speech you should follow the instructions of the chairman. It is useful to repeat the question because sometimes the audience cannot hear it. This also gives you an extra minute to formulate your answer. The length of your answers will vary depending on the number of questions and the time available.

Commitment

"A speech is a solemn responsibility. The man who makes a bad thirty-minute speech to two hundred people wastes only a half hour of his own time. But he wastes one hundred hours of the audience's time - more than four days - which should be a hanging offense." - Jenkin Lloyd Jones

When you agree to give a scientific talk you make a commitment to the audience. You should not accept the invitation to make a talk unless you're willing to make this commitment. This includes preparing your talk and visual aids and preparation to deliver your talk in an effective way. If you deliver a poor talk this reflects poorly on you and will affect your professional standing and career.

Some sources list public speaking as the number one human fear, ranking it higher than fear of death. Professional talks can be stressful because you will be evaluated by your peers, current and future chiefs, and funding agencies. A deep knowledge of your subject and confidence in your research is not enough. You must carefully prepare so that you can give an effective talk. Overconfidence can also be dangerous.

It is important to accurately assess your audience. You must adjust your talk to their level of understanding. Therefore an initial step in preparing a talk is to learn as much as possible about the audience. You should know how large the group will be, whether they will be experts in your field, and the ratio of experts to nonexperts. Of course it's easier to speak to a homogeneous group consisting of all experts or all nonexperts.

A bigger problem arises when you must address a mixed group. In this case, if you make your talk too easy, the experts will feel insulted and if you make your talk at a high level the nonexperts will be frustrated because they cannot understand. One solution is to devote half your time to an introduction of the subject and to save the highly technical material for the second half of your talk. Another approach is to give the technical material first and then to summarize or restate the information in simple, plain English.

Of course, when you accept an invitation to talk you will determine the date, time and place of your talk and how long you have to speak. It is important that you mark your commitments to speak on your calendar so that you will be reminded to prepare in time and to show up. It is also important to know about the rest of the program at the conference. For example will it be talks on other subjects or focused on one subject? Also is useful to know what topics will be given in the same session and what topics precede and follow your talk. If you are the first speaker in a series of talks on a related subject, your presentation should probably include definitions, historical background, underlying assumptions and an introduction to the topic. However, if you are the final speaker, a summary and review of the topic are appropriate. If your talk is scheduled right before lunch, right after lunch, at the end of the day, or at the end of the meeting, you will have a challenge in holding the attention of your audience.

Before you prepare the talk you must define your purpose, topic and appropriate depth. Normally the topic is defined with the invitation to speak. The depth and scope of your speech will be determined in large part by the audience and by the time allowed to you. And you should not overlook the fact that effective communication requires both sending and receiving of information. If you are enthusiastic and fascinated by your subject, these emotions will be transmitted to your audience and will capture their imagination and attention.

In preparing your talk it is useful to ask yourself several questions. Why would other scientists or clinicians be interested in this topic? How can I generate excitement in my topic? How will my audience use the information I am presenting? Is there an anecdote that I can include to add interest or humor?

The key ingredient of a successful scientific talk is clarity. This means that your talk must be well organized and structured in a logical fashion. A common mistake of inexperienced speakers is to try to include too much material and excessive detail in their presentation. It is important for you to avoid going into side topics. Rather you should focus on the main topic of your talk. The introduction should be short and only necessary details of the methods should be given. When presenting mathematical equations or symbols it is important to slow down the pace of your talk and make sure that you explain them clearly. You should talk your audience through your mathematical equation. If your presentation includes mathematical formulas and calculations you may wish to prepare a handout for the audience. Then your oral presentation can concentrate on the relevance of the mathematics to the scientific problem at hand.

Scientific talks are usually serious, but a little humor can vary the rhythm and elicit a favorable response from the audience. However this should not be overdone.

Some think that it is advisable to write every word that you plan to say while others are opposed to this. The accepted style of most scientific meetings is for the speaker to give his talk referring only to notes and slides. It is assumed that he knows his topic very well and that he does not have to read his presentation.

However a written draft can improve the presentation for some speakers. A written draft helps the speaker organize his sentences and may allow him to include more vivid and expressive words. One approach is to write the paper out completely but then to deliver it in a spontaneous manner without actually reading it. In any case you should rehearse your talk several times before a mirror, friendly colleagues, or with a tape recorder. Another advantage of writing out your talk is that this allows you to work on shortening it. When writing your talk you want to make every word count. Also talks should be written to be delivered to the ear and not to the eye. People do not listen the same way that they read.

Do not run overtime. "Be sincere; be brief; be seated." stated Franklin D. Roosevelt. It is rude to exceed your specified time. You should not try to squeeze a 20-minute talk into a 10-minute timeframe. The talk must be designed from the beginning to fit within the 10-minute period. The limited time can actually help you prepare a more effective talk. It forces you to eliminate unnecessary material, which would detract from your message in any case. Every word, table, equation, and figure must contribute to your point and to the purpose of your talk.

It is probably a good idea to prepare your talk to be a few minutes shorter than your allowed time. This is because when you reach the podium you will need extra time to adjust the microphone and to start your slides. You should have one slide, which delivers your closing message and summary. If you then reach the end of your allowed time you can skip ahead to this slide and present your conclusions. Even when you run out of time it is not helpful to close your talk by saying "I think I'll stop here" because this sends a message that you have not prepared. It is better to provide a few words of conclusion and summary and then to stop.

Practice

Rehearsals are very important. You should read to your talk several times. The goal is to achieve a comfortable, confident, conversational style. It is helpful to tape record or videotape your practice session and to review it. You should also practice with your slides to make sure you can handle them well and can coordinate them with your talk.

Handouts

Handouts are useful for complex presentations and can provide important information, summaries, and references. Handouts can be given out before, during, or after the talk and there are advantages and disadvantages to each of these approaches. It is difficult give out handouts during your presentation because this distracts from the presentation and require may require that you briefly stop your presentation. In any case you lose momentum. If you plan to give out your handout at the end of the talk please let the audience know this and also know what will be in the handout. If your handout contains material that cannot be shown on a slide but which is important to the talk, you may wish to give it out before the presentation.

Slides and Visual Aids

Poorly prepared visual aids can ruin your speech. Visual aids should be used to enhance and facilitate the understanding of your spoken words. When your slide is being shown it becomes the focal point of the attention of the audience. Poorly prepared slides indicate to the audience that you have not prepared your talk well or that you do not care about them. This can give an impression of rudeness. To avoid this, the slides must be legible and visible to the entire audience. In addition a dark room is an invitation to the audience to sleep and they may do so if the talk is not interesting.

There are simple guidelines that should be followed when preparing slides. Every visual aid or slide must support the topic covered in your talk. You should ask 3 questions about every slide. 1) Will it add to the presentation? 2) Does it relate to the material covered in the talk? 3) Is the quality acceptable? The answer to each of these questions must be yes. If not, then the slide should be removed. You should not include slides that are not relevant to the talk because this confuses the audience. The connection between each slide and your talk must be clear. Not every point in your talk requires a slide. Of course, there are many areas in which slides are quite useful such as the presentation of numerical data with graphs or charts.

All information presented in your slides must be brief and concise. Here you try to achieve a balance between too much and too little. You do not need to use complete sentences in your slides. A title for each slide gives the audience a clear indication of what the slide is. Word slides should have no more than 36 words and should have a maximum of 6 lines. Use bar graphs or column charts for comparisons and use pie charts for percentages. Correlations can be shown by bar graphs or scatterplots.

The slides must be visible and legible to the entire audience. A visual aid that cannot be read is no aid at all. For example, when you use an overhead projector, you should use the upper portion of projector because this is easier to see from the back of the room. Slides work better in larger rooms than transparencies. Modern computer-generated slides and graphics are usually of sufficient quality to make adequate slides for large meeting rooms.

It is best to left justify the text and leave the right margins ragged. You should use uniform bold typeface. Sans-serif typefaces are generally better. A combination of upper and lower case is easier to read. You can use a larger typeface for headings and a smaller typeface for subheadings to show the relative importance of different material.

Each slide or image should only contain 2 to 3 facts or points of information. If possible you should avoid using complex slides. It is much better to have several simple slides to build up a complex point. Colors can be used in your presentation to emphasize certain points or to distinguish points from each other. Colored backgrounds can make some figures difficult to see -- so you must exercise caution. You should also avoid the temptation to use too many different colors. Certain color combinations are better than others.

When giving your talk you should not read your slides to the audience. The audience can read faster than you can speak. Also if you read your slides this means you may be turning away from the audience, which is something you should generally not do. Each slide should be shown for a certain period of time. This depends on how long it takes you to explain it but also on how long it takes for the audience to absorb the information. It is frustrating for the audience if you move to the next slide before the audience has time to read and comprehend a complex slide. Likewise you should not start talking about the next point while leaving the slide from the previous point on the screen. When using an overhead projector you should not leave the projector empty between transparencies because this puts a bright white light on the screen.

These factors require that you rehearse your talk with your slides in order to make a smooth presentation. When starting your talk it is better not to start immediately with a slide. After you take the podium, establish yourself with the audience, dim the lights and then show the first slide. You must remember to point to the information on the screen and then to turn back to the audience as you speak. When you point to information on your slides, you tell the audience why it is important. Of course, you must maintain momentum and your train of thought as you do this. Handling transparencies while doing all these things takes some practice. One thing that you must do is to make sure that you put the transparencies on the projector correctly so that they are not reversed or backward. When you show slides on an overhead projector you must stand aside after positioning each transparency so that the slide projects properly. The handling of transparencies with an overhead projector requires more practice and skill than computer slides.

As a speaker, you are responsible for learning what audiovisual equipment will be available and to request the equipment that you will need. Generally, you will be able to learn what kind of projector will be available in advance. Small details about how the room is set up such as the position of the podium relative to the screen and whether or not the podium has a reading light can best be ascertained by visiting the room while it is vacant during one of the conference breaks before your talk. Even though a pointer may be provided, I suggest that you always bring your own laser pointer with fresh batteries. This is easy to do and will be useful if the pointer in the room does not work for any reason.

The Delivery of Your Talk

Studies of communication show that nonverbal communication including facial expressions and body language is very important. The tone or quality of your voice is also very important. These two factors may be more important than the actual content of the words you speak. You should strive to use a conversational tone in your speech. Try to make eye contact with some members of the audience. You should try to sense whether or not your talk is being understood and well received by your audience. If they seem to be losing focus you may wish to increase the pace. It's important for you to smile during your talk. You should vary the pace of your talk and also include some pauses. Try to have a relaxed posture. You want to avoid giving the impression of nervousness but also avoid being too casual.

After you give your speech you must remain alert for the question and answers. In order to encourage your audience to ask questions you can ask for them in a way that suggests you expect questions. For example, "what questions do you have?" is better than "any questions?" You should always restate questions from the floor. In a large rooms the questions may not be heard by the entire audience. This allows you to rephrase the question. If you receive a negative question, you can rephrase it in a positive way. It also gives you more time to formulate your reply.

In general you will respond simply and directly to most questions. You should not allow yourself to get sidetracked. If you do not know the answer to a question you should not try to bluff. You can answer with a statement that this is outside your area of expertise. You should also never lose your temper or respond defensively or with anger. You can always offer to discuss your presentation after the meeting. Your goal is not to get dragged into a debate. In any case there is not sufficient time.

If someone asks about something already covered in your talk, in general you should answer this anyway. It is possible that you did not make the point clearly enough. You can to try to present the point in a different way. If someone asks a question that has already been answered, you can state that this point has already been covered. Another common situation occurs when the questioner will try to turn a question into a long-winded speech. In this case you should politely but firmly stop him. You may also get a completely irrelevant question. To this you can respond that this is not really part of your topic. If you run out of time you can apologize for being not being able to take every question. You can also always offer to make yourself available after your presentation. To close the question-and-answer session you can give a short statement and thank your audience.

Conference Proceedings

Many professional societies also publish the proceedings of their conferences. This may include the agenda, abstracts submitted, transcripts of oral presentations, or invited papers. Medical writers may work for the publishing house and be involved in the planning and editing of the conference proceedings. Materials presented at scientific meetings may be at risk for redundant publication. This is because the presenters will also wish to publish their work in a peer-reviewed journal. Also the abstract forms from professional meetings quite often contain a statement that the author must sign that the work will not be presented at another similar meeting. Most primary journals will still publish scientific papers that have been presented at scientific meetings on the theory that the presentation at the meeting does not constitute full publication. However, this is an area of possible ethical conflict and the medical writer may have to remind the authors of their ethical responsibilities.

Clinical trials

Readers need to know a large number of details about how a clinical trial was designed, executed, and analyzed before they will incorporate the results into their clinical practice. If the reader wishes to prepare a review or a meta-analysis they will need even more details. The title must include all the main elements of the trial. The introduction section will be similar to a standard research paper and must answer the question: why did you start? The methods section will include file design, trial organization, study procedures study participants, interventions, measurements monitoring, data collection and assessment. This must include the methods for masking or blinding of treatment. The primary outcome measure must be specified.

The results section will specify how many participants started the protocol in each group and how many completed it. Differences between groups must be specified in absolute terms as well as percentages. The distributions of the outcome measures must also be given. Any effect of confounding variables must be discussed. Adverse effects in the groups must also be noted.

The discussion will depend on the complexity of the trial and its results. Evidence supporting the answer of the trial from other trials should also be presented in the discussion along with any counterevidence.

Observational studies of diagnostic tests

These reports must include the spectrum of patients studied. Also the definition of the disease or syndrome for which the test was applied must be given. Any study subgroups must be specified. Any possibilities for bias must be mentioned and the safeguards against this bias must be described. Indeterminate findings must be included in the data. The test and observer reliability is must be adequately documented and considered.

Meta-analysis

A meta-analysis opens with an introductory section and continues with a detailed description of the methods and procedures. These methods must include the criteria for including studies. These criteria must be objective. In addition the methods used to find studies must be given. The introduction will state why the meta-analysis was launched. The methods section must include the following: Did you have a formal working protocol? How was the literature search conducted? Did you search for unpublished trials? How were trials included or excluded? How were the data extracted from the trial reports? What outcomes were considered? What detailed statistical procedures were used? The discussion will summarize the main findings, assess possible weaknesses in the analysis, weigh findings against other meta-analyses, resolve conflicting judgments, suggest any clinical implications, and suggest further research.

Publication of Case Reports

Case Reports

Case reports allow the clinician to communicate findings from an individual patient to an audience of clinicians. Sometimes findings from a single patient can have implications for the pathophysiology of a certain disease and merit publication in peer-reviewed journal. In general, case reports are shorter and may be subject to special requirements by the journal.

Publication of a case report is quite often the first type of paper a physician will try to write in the early stages of his or her career. In general, clinical studies, with a series of patients in a planned study design are valued much more highly. Many journals refuse to publish case reports or publish a limited number of such reports. Often, such cases are placed at the end of a journal. The journal where you submit your case report should be chosen with care.

There has been a gradual shift in medical teaching at universities from theory to clinical analysis over the past 100 years. In the last century improved methods in pathology and histology more clearly explain the underlying disease. Biochemical advances brought new laboratory methods for detecting disease and its effects. With these advances, the case report became an important part of clinical teaching and of the medical literature. The great increase in clinical investigation over recent years has led to a flood of competing papers. Single cases are becoming less and less acceptable for publication.

However some kinds of case reports still merit publication. These include unique cases that may represent a new syndrome or disease, a case with an unexpected association of two more diseases that may represent a previously unsuspected etiologic relationship, a case that represents important variations from the expected pattern, or a case with an unusual evolution that suggests an important therapeutic or adverse drug effect. Case reports can also be useful to develop hypotheses, to reveal difficult diagnostic issues or novel treatment approaches, and to identify clinical and research needs for the future.

Authors who wish to prepare case reports must be aware that it is sometimes very difficult to get these published in first-rate journals. However, cases can sometimes be more easily published as a concise letter-to-the-editor.

An acute and well-informed clinician sometimes may see a patient with a disease manifestation that is so unusual that it cannot be accounted for by known diseases or syndromes. This may be a patient with some specific chemical disorder, perhaps the result of an enzyme malfunction on a genetic basis. Sometimes one finds two uncommon diseases in the same patient and depending on the circumstances this may suggest that there is some pathophysiologic relationship between them.

A well-written case report can be a valuable contribution to the medical literature. In order to be publishable, a case report should describe some new or rare finding associated with a disease, a new association between diseases and symptoms, an unexpected event in the course of treatment or observation, new findings that help explain the pathogenesis of a disease, or a unique approach to therapy.

Journals differ widely in their policies regarding case reports, so it is essential to read the instructions to authors that pertain to this type of report. Differing journals may require the report to be formatted in different ways or may indicate that they do not accept case reports at all. In general the format is introduction, case presentation, discussion, and conclusions. The introduction must state why the case is being reported. Usually this means indicating why the case is unusual or how it contributes to medical knowledge.

In some ways research papers are easier to write than case reports. Case reports have a complex structure. A case report will include a statement of why the case is important, a description of the case with all pertinent data, discussion of the reasons why this case is unique or unexpected, alternative explanations for these unique features, and a conclusion with clinical implications. The introduction of the paper will explain the reason why the case is being reported. The actual description of the case and can be given in several formats. Usually the most straightforward is a chronological sequence. Relevant, and only the relevant data should be given. If there is a large amount of data sometimes it can be more effectively presented in table format. Usually the case description is followed immediately by the discussion. The discussion will contain your argument or reasons why this case is unique. It is not sufficient to say that a search of literature failed to find any similar cases. The author must specify how the search was conducted.

The case presentation itself should be short and to the point. A standard approach to reporting the history and physical should be taken; however, irrelevant facts from parts of the history should be omitted. The normal order is chief complaint, presenting symptoms, prior relevant illnesses, past medical history, relevant family history, medications, allergies, social history (if relevant), noteworthy finding on physical exams and laboratory tests, differential diagnosis, final diagnosis or diagnoses, treatment and follow-up. The case should be described clearly, briefly, and results of laboratory investigations presented. If unusual laboratory investigations are done, the normal values should also be given. One or 2 figures may be appropriate here, but the number of figures may be limited by the instructions to authors. The patient should never be identified and his or her initials should not be given.

The discussion should document the scientific purpose and clarify the new information contributed by the reports, provide evidence for the conclusions, and explain clinical, theoretical, and/or research implications. The discussion should provide well-presented and organized evidence to support your diagnosis and recommendations. Other possible explanations for the findings should be considered fairly. The implications and relevance of the findings should also be discussed and future directions for research or for patient care considered. References for each of these points must be provided, however, bear in mind that the instructions to authors may limit the number of references that you are allowed to use in a case report. This may mean that you have to cite a few carefully selected review articles instead of individual studies. If you state that a literature search did not uncover any prior cases, you should give some information about the type of search that you did. For example, how far back in time did your search, what database was used (Medline), etc.

Case Series Reports

This is a retrospective analysis of medical records of similar cases usually collected at one hospital or institution. Often, case series papers have value because they report the entire spectrum of a disease and its manifestations. If the case series analysis is carried out with sufficient depth and intellectual analysis it may take the form of a research paper.

Editorial, Book review, and Letter-to-the-editor

The Editorial

At one time the term editorial indicated that the article was a message from the journal's editor. This is no longer true and today editorials are usually written by others. They also serve many other functions. Editorials may comment on an original paper in the current issue of the journal and may put the paper into perspective with other recently reported findings. The editorial may speculate on the clinical or future implications of the paper. Some editorials take political positions and others may cite extensive evidence so much that they take on the character of a research paper.

Editorials do not have a clear structure like research papers. Is useful to keep in mind the need to present a critical argument. The writer must choose an issue or question, then review the evidence, pose possible answers, assess counterevidence and present a conclusion. Sometimes the conclusion is reached that further studies are needed. A variation of the editorial is the position paper. These papers may be longer and more speculative in nature. For example, such papers are included in the Sounding Board section of the New England Journal of Medicine.

The Book Review

Book reviews are usually invited by the editor. A well-written book review will include a comparison of the book to other books on the same subject. To write a book review requires consideration of whether the book is better than others of its kind and of the audience for whom the book is written. Then the reviewer must consider whether the book meets the needs of that audience. Evidence and counterevidence must be considered. The reader of the book review wants to know whether it is worth the cost of the book. Enough information must be given so the reader can judge whether the book is relevant for his needs.

Letters to the Editor

Letters are easy to write; anyone can write a letter. However to get a letter published in the prestigious medical journal is not so easy. Many letters are miniature versions of research reports, case reports, reviews, or editorials. Care and effort must be taken in the writing of such letters. In cases where you are responding to something that upsets you it is wise to hold off sending a letter for a week or two to avoid sending off an angry or rude letter.

The topics of a letter to the editor can vary greatly. It may be brief findings from a research trial or it may include comments on another paper published in that journal. It can also be a short essay or an editorial piece. When accepting letters commenting on published papers, the journal editors may have certain requirements. For example, they may require that the letter be received within a certain timeframe after the paper is published. They may also request the original authors of the paper to respond to the letter.

Review Articles
"Failure is the beginning of wisdom." William Zinnser

The medical literature is so large that no clinician or scientist can keep up with all of it. We rely on papers that synthesize this data, such as review articles, meta-analysis, editorials, and other summaries. A case-series analysis, which includes a critical review of the case records in the author's practice or institution and a review of literature, is a kind of review paper.

The introduction to a review paper may need to indicate why

the review is needed. The method sections should clearly define the disease or condition under consideration. If a literature search was made, the exact method of the search must also be specified. A review of a disease will likely include the following sections commonly found in textbooks: etiology, pathogenesis, manifestations (clinical, roentgenographic, laboratory) diagnosis, treatment, and prognosis. All the elements of critical argument needed to support the conclusion of a review paper must be presented. A careful review of the topic may identify issues and problems that are currently unresolved and which need further study. Many review articles are longer than research reports and may cover many subtopics.

Review articles are written to provide a perspective on previous work. As with other types of papers, you must catch the reader's interest quickly or your article will not be read. These articles must be understandable to readers who are not experts in the field and must provide useful information (i.e. clinical information). These types of articles may be descriptive, in which case they bring the readers up to date in a certain area that is changing rapidly, or evaluative, in which case they answer a specific question (example: A review titled "Is there a role for digoxin in the treatment of heart failure today?").

Before starting the work on a review paper, it can be very useful to contact the editor of your target journal and ask if the topic is appropriate for that journal and if the editor considers you qualified to write it. As always, you must read the instructions to authors regarding the journal's policies for review articles.

The review paper has less structure and format than a research paper, but tends to be longer. In general, such papers should include the reason for the selection of the topic (what question are you trying to answer), methods used to search the literature and select papers, limitations in the articles reviewed, and most importantly, your conclusions as to what it all means.

Your review must be objective, because the editor and reviewers will be looking for evidence of bias on your part. Because these papers are long, it is best to subdivide them into titled sections or to use an outline format.

Checklist:
1. Who are your readers?
2. Is the purpose of your paper well described?
3. Does the review deal with an issue of interest to these readers?
4. Do you describe how you selected articles for inclusion?
5. What were your methods for evaluating each article? Are these methods adequately described in the paper?
6. Is your assessment of the literature you review free of bias?
7. Were the papers that you reviewed free of bias?

Patient Education Material

This is a rapidly growing area. Medical products, especially new products, need to be explained to the patients who will use them.

Special Media

This can include slide sets (designed to be used by physicians or other medical professionals in their lectures), audio presentations, and video. All of these can be formatted for the Internet or some other computer readable media (i.e. CD-ROM, etc.). The use of the Internet or computer allows creation of interactive presentations or programs that change according to the reader's responses. This can be used to create interactive clinical case presentations that can be used to teach or evaluate clinical decision making. The interactivity available in computer formats has enabled the evolution of a new field and industry, E-learning. E-learning encompasses the use of this technology in education for all types of learning and training.

Continuing Medical Education (CME)

CME are programs or literature that help medical professionals extend their knowledge and keep up to date in their fields. CME is required for physicians to maintain their medical licenses at most states in the United States. It is also increasingly required in other countries. CME programs are created by many professional organizations, including associations of various medical specialties, for example, the American College of Cardiology, etc. CME programs are also created by medical companies to help educate physicians about new drugs or products or new indications for a drug or product. CME programs can focus on a topic, a drug, a journal article, or a case presentation, or sometimes on a certain medical technology, such as imaging or a biochemical test. Sometimes they focus on the development of a specific medical skill. Computer technology has had a major impact this area and CME programs can be presented in a variety of media and formats.

CME programs can also be organized as dinner roundtables, symposia, teleconferences, webcasts, video conferences, and can be quite large with thousands of participants, requiring the use of large conference or hotel facilities. In these types of programs, the content is often created by physicians who are experts in the field. However, many excellent CME programs have been created by medical writers who research a topic and interview experts. In some cases, medical writers take materials created by expert physicians and edit or enhance them for a CME program. When creating programs using computer formats, it is possible to create more complex programs that provide feedback to the participant.

CME programs include a description of the authors, who must give disclosures of any financial relationships that they may have with medical industry. The CME programs will typically specify a number of credit hours that they provide to the participant. This is based on the amount of time that it takes to complete the program. The programs will often include a short quiz or test at the end to assess if the participants understand the material. They also include a survey in which the participants give feedback on the program quality.

References

Begg C et al. Improving the quality of reporting randomized clinical trials: the CONSORT statement. JAMA 1996:276:637-639.

Applying research evidence to individual patients: Evidence based case reports will help. Godlee F. BMJ 1998;316:1621-1622 (Editorial)

Hill AB. The reasons for writing. Br Med J 1965;2:870.

Chapter 6. Resources for Authors

Uniform Requirements for Manuscripts Submitted to Biomedical Journals

http://www.icmje.org/recommendations/

Resources for Medical Writers

Articles for Medical Writers

Continuous quality improvement and the process of writing for academic publication
http://www.ncbi.nlm.nih.gov/entrez/query.fcgi?cmd=Retrieve&db=PubMed&list_uids=10947385&dopt=Abstract

Bordage G Reasons reviewers reject and accept manuscripts: the strengths and weaknesses in medical education reports. Acad Med 2001 Sep;76(9):889-96.
Bordage G. Reasons reviewers reject and ..[PMID:11553504]

Internationalization of general surgical journals: origin and content of articles published in North America and Great Britain from 1983 to 1998.
Tompkins RK, Ko CY, Donovan AJ.Arch Surg 2001 Dec;136(12):1345-51
Tompkins RK, et al. Internationalization of gener...[PMID:11735855]

Exorcising the millionaire in the lab next door. Caveman A. J Cell Sci 2000 Oct;113 (Pt 19):3351-2

Links for Medical Writers

The following is a collection of links to web pages useful to medical authors. I have made efforts to make sure that all of these links work and that they are up to date, but the internet is an ever-changing place and some of them may not work.

Medline/PubMed

The most important tool used by medical writers is probably the MEDLINE database. This database includes bibliographic data and abstracts of the biomedical literature from 1966 to the present. There are several ways to get to Medline at no cost using the web. Perhaps the most popular is thru PubMed at:

http://www.ncbi.nlm.nih.gov/PubMed/

Cochrane Collaboration

The Cochrane Reviews are systematic assessments of the evidence of the effects of medical treatments and are intended to help medical professionals and patients make informed decisions about health care based on the evidence. These reviews have significant impact on practice, policy decisions and research worldwide. They are published electronically in the Cochrane database of systematic reviews by John Wiley & Sons, as part of the Cochrane Library. The Cochrane Library is a collection of high quality evidence-based databases, with immediate access to over 2000 full text articles. It is published every three months and is available by subscription, on the Internet, and on CD-ROM. Many countries have national subscriptions to the Cochrane Library, which allows everyone in that country to have free access. The number of countries with these subscriptions is increasing.

Abstracts of the reviews are freely available to everyone via the Internet.

http://www.cochrane.org

CARE Case Report Guidelines

The **CARE** guidelines, developed by an international group of experts, are designed to increase the accuracy, transparency, and usefulness of case reports.

http://www.care-statement.org/

Email Journal Updates

Free email updates from journals in your field from Amedeo. com. This is the same company that produces the listing of free medical journals online.

http://www.amedeo.com

Public Library of Science

Information about "open access" journals.

http://www.plos.org

Free Medical Journals Online

Not all journals allow full text access online, but most of the ones that do are listed here.

http://www.freemedicaljournals.com

Association of Medical Illustrators

http://www.ami.org/

Books for Medical Writers

How to Report Statistics in Medicine: Annotated Guidelines for Authors, Editors, and Reviewers

Edited by Thomas Lang and Michelle Secic. American College of Physicians; 2nd edition (August 30, 2006)

This book provides detailed guidelines for the clear presentation of statistical results in your scientific paper. Although the authors do not emphasize how to do the statistical analysis, they do show how to clearly present statistical analyses such as descriptive data, sampling, multiple variable reporting, meta-analyses, Bayesian analyses, and clinical outcomes.

American Medical Association Manual of Style: A Guide for Authors and Editors

Edited by Iverson C and Flanagin A. Hardcover - 10th edition (March 2007) Lippincott, Williams & Wilkins.

Manual of guidelines for medical writing written in outline format.

Writing and Speaking for Excellence: A Guide for Physicians

by D. St. James

The ability to write and speak in a concise, well-organized way is a skill not often taught in medical schools. This 263-page textbook that addresses the most frequently asked questions physicians have about medical writing and oral presentations and offers practical solutions. The author has worked with more than 7,000 physician writers and speakers, and has conducted seminars at hundreds of medical centers and universities.

Organizations for the Medical Writer

The American Medical Writer's Association (AMWA) has an annual meeting and a journal for medical writers. The journal contains many useful articles for medical writers. These include "how to" articles on various aspects of medical writing.

http://www.amwa.org

Index

Made in United States
North Haven, CT
02 November 2021

10789175R00095